THE BRAE HOUSE

Xmas 83.

THE BRAE HOUSE

Millie Sutherland

JOHN CALDER * LONDON
RIVERRUN PRESS * DALLAS

First published in 1979 by John Calder (Publishers) Ltd.,
18 Brewer Street, London W1R 4AS and in 1980 by
Riverrun Press Inc., Dallas, Texas

ISBN 0 7145 3646 6   casebound

Library of Congress Catalog No. 79-66051

Typeset in 11 pt. Baskerville by Gloucester Typesetting Co. Ltd.

Printed in Great Britain by M. & A. Thomson Litho.

Bound in Great Britain by Hunter & Foulis Ltd.

THE BRAE HOUSE

Chapter 1

I was three years old when I arrived. I was tired as I had come a long journey, from Aberdeen to be exact, up to Glenurquhart. I was an orphan and was being boarded out to a foster parent. The tall, gaunt woman who brought me, spoke to my foster mother. A few moments later I was handed over. The woman turned, entered the car which brought me, said something to the two men inside and then drove away. These three people had been my only companions these last two days. I couldn't have been very happy at the orphanage, for when they came to take me away, I remember feeling glad. But now, standing outside The Brae House, the only feeling I had was of fear and desolation. I began to cry.

'I am Anne Gordon,' a sharp voice said, and my hand was gripped until it hurt. 'Stop that crying and come inside.' Trailing behind I entered the cottage. 'Here she is, Duncan,' pushing me forward, 'her name is Mina Forbes.'

The man she called Duncan sat in a high backed chair with crutches resting on either side. White hair topped a face full of warmth and love, and when he smiled, it was as if the sun had entered the small room.

'Come, child,' he said, and lifted me on his knee.

I loved him from that moment.

'Give her something to eat, Anne, and put her to bed, she must be very tired coming from Aberdeen to Inverness and up here to the Glen.'

God bless you, Duncan. You are long gone, but you gave me the first feeling I ever had of being wanted.

Probably I gave a sigh. I was home. Not somewhere to be sheltered and then returned to the Orphanage. Not that. But a home full of love. I had come to the Brae House.

Chapter 2

The Brae House was one of five cottages in a small village, if you could call it that, called Balgreig, two miles off the main road running from Inverness to Glen Affric. Although Balgreig was small, the District was quite large with small crofts surrounding it. The Brae House was a small croft, and as Duncan was a semi-invalid, the McAndrews and McDonalds, families whose land surrounded ours, worked it for him along with Aunt Anne, as I was told to call her, and she worked as hard as any man.

I wasn't the only orphan in Balgreig. Nearly every house had some, mostly from Glasgow. Some were treated as if they were members of the family while others were treated like slaves, out in the morning helping with the croft before they did the two mile hike to school. The same ritual when they returned at night. When the Authorities discovered what was going on, or it was reported to them, the children were taken away, but after a time the same homes were given other children, as the demand for foster homes was great. This never happened in the few cottages beside us. The McAndrews, McDonalds, the Frasers and McMillans all had children of their own and one or two foster children, who, on the whole, were well treated.

The kitchen of my new home was the largest room in the house. The floor was paved with flag stones with a home-made rug at the hearth. The fire was made of peat and cooking was done by hanging the pots from a sway—a large hook which was hinged from a large piece of sheet iron screwed into the stone-work of the chimney breast. The sway itself has holes running up vertically at three inch intervals so that the height of the pot from the fire could be adjusted. The swing or sway and the controlled height gave splendid control over cooking tempera-tures. The baking was done by girdle, a flat sheet of cast iron which was hung from the sway. Scones, pancakes, oatcakes were all baked over twigs or acorns which were gathered by us children in the woods. This was supposed to give a better flavour to the baking, especially the oatcakes.

Duncan's bedroom, as he could no longer climb the stairs, was through from the kitchen and contained just a bed, chest of drawers and a chair. Between the kitchen and the outside door was another room which, I suppose, could be called a parlour.

This room contained the most furniture, with a large double bed, a horsehair sofa and two horsehair chairs. A high mantle-piece flagged the wall and a chest of drawers with a mirror above it served as a dressing table. A small hand basin and ewer stood on a marble stand. There was waxcloth on the floor and another home-made rug at the fireplace. As this room was never used, except at New Year or when important people, like the minister or teacher arrived, the fire was never lit. Apart from a beautiful crochet bedspread and a few ornaments adorning the mantlepiece, there was no other decoration.

The attics were reached by a wooden stair opposite the outside door. They were small rooms with only a skylight serving as a window, very cold in winter and sweltering hot in summer, for the roof was made of corrugated iron. A bed, a home-made dressing table and a chest of drawers, where most of our clothes were kept, were the only furnishings the attics contained. Lying in bed, I loved listening to the pit-pat the raindrops made on the roof. It was my only lullaby.

Aunt Anne and I slept together when I was small. It was only when I became a teenager that I was allowed to have the other attic bedroom to myself. I was constantly reminded of who I was by this woman who had undertaken the task of my upbringing.

Anne Gordon was a hard, hard woman. Never did her laughter ring through the house, never did a word of endearment pass her lips. I often wondered at this. She was both fair and just and I feared and respected her. I was only three years old, but one look from those steel grey eyes was enough to banish any thought other than obedience from my mind. I still don't know how I would have fared under the harsh discipline and leather hand of Aunt Anne if Uncle Dunk hadn't been there. He stopped me from getting many a thrashing. It was Uncle Dunk, my pet name for him, who told me stories before going to bed, as I sat gazing up in wonder or resting my head on his knee.

He spoke in the Gaelic, which I soon picked up. Actually, by the time I went to school, I had forgotten how to speak anything else.

His stories enthralled me. He told me about the Highlands and their beauty, the history of their mountains, Bens, Lochs and Rivers. He told me about the coming and going of the Romans. Speaking of the Romans, he took great pains to tell me they never conquered the Highlands. He spoke sadly of Glencoe and about the Highland Clearances after the Battle of Culloden. He told me of the coming of Bonnie Prince Charlie, from his arrival at Moidart until his defeat at Culloden. In his beautiful soft Gaelic voice he spoke simply to me, so that I gould grasp the full meaning of his words. I could visualise the coming and going of the Romans, and I could see Bonnie Prince Charlie tramping the hills in full Highland dress. I was of course too young to understand the gravity of his quest and the consequences of his defeat.

I soon forgot that I was born in Aberdeen, that I was ever in an orphanage. This was my home. My Highlands and my Glen. It all started at Uncle Dunk's knee and was to last a lifetime.

Chapter 3

It was September, 1918. I was ready for school. Clothes arrived from the Aberdeen Authorities. Underclothes, two frocks, one for school and one for Sunday; a Sunday coat and one for school, one or two cotton pinafores to keep my clothes clean and two pairs of boots, again one pair for school and one pair for Sunday, but on this lovely September morning, I was barefoot like all the children. Boots were only worn from October until May.

My clothes were miles too big, but as Aunt Anne said, 'You will grow.' *Style* was a word unknown to me. My clothes were donned with a stiff warning, 'Look after them. The Authorities have more to do with their money than clad you.'

I was to be escorted to school by two boys of the McDonalds, who had four other children. Two girls, Florence and Betty Kelly, and Joseph and John Gardener. As Joe and John were a few years older, I was put into their care. We were joined by the Fraser orphans and two of the Frasers' own children, Andrew and Tom. Jenny and David Simpson were the foster children. The McAndrew children were Nan, Peter and Mary, the foster children were Bob and Willie Whitelaw. The McMillans had just one foster boy, Tom Madden, who left School not long after I started. Mrs McMillan took no more after Tom, as she said she was getting too old and had had many children in her day who were now scattered all over the world.

The road to school was all downhill, two and a half miles distant. It was a two roomed building with the Headmaster's house adjoining on the main road to Inverness. There was only one other teacher, a Miss Ross and I was one of her pupils. How on earth did Mr Geddes and his one teacher cope with three classes each. But teach us they did. Sixty per cent were foster children from all the crofts and farms in the district, the other 40 per cent were children from the Glen. The Glen children could be picked out a mile away by their clothes. Instead of boots they had shoes. The clothes were of finer material and brighter coloured. Not like our own worsted cloth, heavy and dull, browns and greys.

We were humiliated and scorned. 'Tramps, tinks, paupers.' The jibes and the jeers were thrown at us by the Glen children. If we retaliated in any way, we were severely punished by Mr Geddes, the headmaster, for the parents of the Glen children protested strongly.

Apart from that, I seemed to do all right at my books, as Uncle Dunk called my education. At night, after my dinner, he would draw my stool over beside him.

'What were you taught today lass? Show me your book.' My ABC was produced, laid on his knee and I pointed out with my finger what we had learned.

'Ach, I can't go this English at all,' he said with a puzzled frown. 'Neither can I,' I giggled.

The majority of us had to learn English before we could even start to learn arithmetic, history or geography. The Gaelic was not allowed in school unless on the curriculum, and it certainly wasn't at Dalreigh School. Uncle learned me in the Gaelic and my teacher taught me in English, so I had the best of both worlds, and it wasn't long before I became expert at both languages.

The two and a half mile hike back uphill from school was a mammoth task for my small legs. I was shown no mercy as the other children had already learned the hard way. 'Keep your eyes on the ground for sharp stones, watch out for nettles in the grass, keep your bag well up on your back. Its easier that way.' So said Joe Gardener. He was my knight in shining armour. Whenever the going got too rough and I started lagging behind, I was hoisted on his back. To be carried even 100 yards was refreshing. School buses or taxis just didn't exist.

School started at 10 o'clock, so we were away from nine in the morning until five at night. I carried a piece to school, two or three slices of bread, butter and sugar or jam, never anything else. If bread was short, scones or pancakes sufficed and a bottle of milk, about half a pint. So it goes without saying, we were starving when we got home.

All in all, I was well fed. Breakfast consisted of oatmeal porridge and a cup of hot cocoa and an oatcake bannock. At night when I came home from school there was always soup, especially in winter. Boiled beef with plenty of potatoes and vegetables was followed by a milk pudding. Where Aunt Anne got her milk, I don't remember. As we were the only family without a cow, I presume she got it from whoever grazed their livestock on our small piece of land. Money never passed hands all the years I was at Balgreig, not even to the horse-drawn vans that came once in a while to the village. A sheep or a pig or eggs seemed to be bartered for flour and meal. The bare essentials were all stored in kists, large wooden trunks in the kitchen. These were covered with a piece of oilcloth and the water pails sat on the top. The well where we drew our water was fifty yards from the house. I never knew it to dry up or freeze and it served the five homes in Balgreig.

After my chores I was allowed out to play. I had no ball or doll, but Mary McAndrew, the McAndrew's daughter, had, so my instinct took me to the McAndrew's house. I wasn't allowed in, but had to wait on the doorstep until Mary's mother allowed her out. Mary and I got on well together. I never heard her call me names like her brother Peter and her oldest sister Nan. Sometimes all the 'crowd' as we called each other came to what we called 'The Green' to play.

The Green, about three to four acres, was the focal point for us kids. The boys played football but everyone joined in for games like cricket, rounders and hares and hounds. Balgreig crofts were built in a semi-circle around the Green with pasture land and outbuildings to the rear. The McAndrews, the first nearest the road leading to the school, had the largest croft, about 80 to 100 acres.

We seldom ventured beyond the Green. Behind the crofts and beyond the fields were moors and mountains, including a loch. It wasn't until I was eight or nine years old that I ventured beyond the Green to a whole new world of breathtaking beauty. It was then I put away childish things and became a loner, even in school.

I learnt quickly and enjoyed every minute of my schooldays, and when I was eight I entered Mr Geddes's classroom. I also learned to skate, getting a pair of Mary McAndrew's skates when they got too small for her. This was just to get to school in winter. When I asked Aunt Anne for skates when the ones I had been given became too small, I was looked at as if I had asked for the moon.

'You keep your place my girl,' was the reply. 'Do you think you are one of the Glen children?' They were given skates by their parents and lost no education like the foster children, when the road was covered with frozen snow. The foster parents thought it a waste of money to buy skates, as at fourteen, the foster children never or seldom went on from school to higher education.

'I can't buy you skates,' said Aunt Anne. 'I don't have the money and the Authorities would never hear of it. Anyway, I won't be asking them.'

The Authorities, The Authorities! How I hated those words. Who were these nameless, faceless people anyhow, who clad me in dull browns and greys, with tackety boots on my feet and thick black woollen stockings, who would never dream of buying me skates to get to school when the snow was frozen and it was impossible to walk the two and a half miles. I was soon to find out.

It was a Saturday morning. Up till now, the weather had held. It was cold, but no snow had fallen, and it was the second week of November. Saturday was always a busy day for us as it was the Sabbath next day. No work was done on the Sunday, neither cooking nor dish-washing nor housework of any kind. I was not allowed to make beds or sew or knit. That Saturday I was outside, scraping the big kettle and pots before they were black leaded and polished, when Mary came running to the gate. 'Mina, there's a car coming along the road.'

A car coming to Balgreig was an event. The last car that had arrived was the one which had brought me a few years ago, and I understood it had caused quite a stir then. By the time Mary stopped speaking, the car, a big black one, had passed Mary's house and was approaching our gate. It stopped. Two men got out and I immediately recognised one of them as the gentleman who had brought me to the Glen. I turned and fled into the house.

'Uncle Dunk,' I screamed. 'Don't let them take me away, please, please Uncle Dunk, I don't want to go.'

Aunt Anne by this time had met the gentlemen and brought them to the Big Room. I was standing behind Uncle Dunk's chair.

'Come out from behind that chair, Mina. These gentlemen want to speak to you,' Aunt Anne said, as she entered the kitchen followed by the two men. I looked at Uncle Dunk. The terror I felt must have been shown on my face as he turned his head towards me. I could see his eyes and they were twinkling. His voice was soft and warm as he said, 'Come lassie, no one is going to take you away.' I slowly came round to the side of his chair and gripped one of his knarled hands. The two men looked on in silence for a moment. The one who had brought me said, 'Show us your school books, Mina.' I let go Uncle Dunk's hand and slipped behind his chair. My school bag was lying on my stool which was always placed there when not in use.

'Quickly girl,' the other man spoke harshly, 'we want to get back to Inverness before dark.'

Aunt Anne grabbed my bag and handed it over. In silence,

my books were studied by the two men and handed back to Aunt Anne.

'She seems healthy and quite happy,' one of the men said, eyeing me up and down. Uncle Dunk took my hand and drew me towards him. I was now standing between his legs. Stroking my hair he said, 'We love her very much, don't we, Anne?'

If Aunt Anne at that time had agreed with Uncle Dunk, I would have been the happiest girl in the world. But no, she didn't. Grudgingly she replied, 'Oh, she's not bad. If her mother wants her, I suppose she will have to go.'

My Mother! Who on earth was this? I had never heard of a mother, nor did I want to. Terror seized me again. I clung to Uncle Dunk's legs, tears rolling down my cheeks. 'Don't let her say that. Please, Uncle Dunk, don't let her give me away. I want to stay here. I'll be awfully good always.'

Uncle Dunk couldn't speak. I saw he was swallowing hard, a habit he had when upset. It was Mr Wilson, the man who had looked at my books, who broke the silence that followed. He came over and touched me on the shoulder.

'We are not taking you away, Mina, just came to see if you were getting on all right. Goodbye.' They were gone.

I heard the car moving away and the laughter of the children who ran after it past the McAndrew's farm. Relief flooded the whole of my body. Aunt Anne returned to the kitchen after seeing the visitors away.

'What an exhibition,' she said. 'You wicked girl, get on with your work. Tomorrow is the Sabbath and we have a lot to do.'

'Ssh, Anne,' Uncle Dunk said, 'she's only a child and afraid and doesn't want to leave us.'

Chapter 4

I hated the Sabbath. Breakfast consisted of cocoa and a slice of bread and jam. No porridge was cooked. Hail, rain or shine, we trekked the two miles to the church, 'The Wee Free' as it was called. The way led us through a wood called the 'Plantation' with pine trees so tall that the branches, stretching high above, almost looked as if they reached to the sky. The trees were so thick that no sunlight penetrated through the dense foliage and the path was strewn with pine needles and moss, so thick that any sound was completely muffled.

The older kids took advantage of this and would creep up on us from behind to grab our hats or scarves. Our parents or guardians always seemed to catch us with our hats in our hand, which meant we had to walk beside them the rest of the way, which was very boring indeed.

The Minister, Mr McLennon gave the Gaelic sermon, which lasted two hours. There was no organ in our church. Mr McPherson was our Precentor who started off the hymns. Church went in at 11.30 a.m. and finished at 1.30 p.m. Parents and Guardians then went home and the children stayed for Sunday School until 2.30 p.m. By the time we got home, we were tired and hungry.

After dinner I had to listen to Uncle Dunk reading from the Bible until after four. I didn't mind my Uncle reading a chapter in the morning and one before going to bed, but the Sabbath was different. He just never seemed to stop.

After a cup of tea at six, Aunt Anne and I went down to Dalreich school for the evening service with everyone else from the village. The only excuse for not going was illness. Another hour of a sermon, usually taken by a Lay Preacher, then home to bed at nine o'clock, exhausted. It was a blessed relief when we all went back to school on Monday.

Several weeks later, I received my skates. I think it was during the Christmas Holidays. I never knew how I got them or if they were new, but I was certain Uncle Dunk had a lot to do with it.

Under the tuition of Willie Whitelaw, the McAndrew's foster boy, I learned to skate and by the time school went back after Christmas, I could skate with any Glen boy or girl of my own age and I knew I would be much better as I grew older. Willie Whitelaw and I were the only two orphans with skates, and Willie's were handed down from Peter McAndrew, the eldest son, when his boots outgrew them. Willie certainly worked for anything he got from his foster parents.

About this time, Mary got a pony from her father. Peter got one too. Mary was a born rider. But not so Peter. He soon tired of his mare, Jess, and it was left either in the paddock next to their house or turned out to grass at the back of our house.

One day, during the Easter holidays, Mary and I were playing in the field making daisy chains, when she suggested I ride Jess. 'Oh no, Mary, I could never do that,' I gasped.

'Feartie,' she taunted.

'I'm not,' I replied. 'I bet if I learned I could ride as good as you.'

Mary rose and put her daisy chain round her neck. 'Bet you can't.'

'I can and I will,' I said hotly. 'You just watch.' I had also risen but had left my daisy chain on the grass. I approached Jess. She came trotting over expecting a tasty bite. As I couldn't reach her mane, I asked Mary to help me up which she did and I sat on a mare for the first time in my life. I clung to her mane, my legs hardly able to straddle her back. A slap on the rump from Mary, and Jess was off round the field. I held on like grim death. My legs couldn't grip the mare's back and as she made a sharp turn I was thrown onto the grass and winded. Poor Mary thought I was dead, and ran screaming to her mother. Everyone seemed to be bending over me whan I came to. Aunt Anne and Mary's mother said we were to be whipped, but Uncle Dunk stepped in when I was brought into the house.

'Leave her alone. What harm has she done?,' he said, in such a voice of authority that Aunt Anne stared and turned away towards the peat fire.

'Go out for the peat and clogs and don't dally,' she said in a voice which I knew well. Cold and severe.

But this mishap didn't stop me mounting Jess whenever I could. I led her over to the dyke enclosing the field, climbed up and mounted her. I had to bide my time to do this, in case I was seen.

Most late spring and summer evenings, Aunt Anne and Uncle Dunk sat out in the front garden. I used to help him out and arrange his chair where he got the maximum amount of sun. I noticed he was getting less steady on his legs and sat out for shorter spells, so I had to be quick going round the back of the house and into the field where Jess was grazing, have my spin and get back to the front of the house to take Uncle Dunk back in to his chair. Naturally, once or twice I was caught!

After school one day, I mounted Jess. I was no sooner up when I heard a deep booming voice behind me. 'Come down from there.'

I swung round to face Andrew McAndrew, Mary's father. I obeyed meekly.

'Who told you to ride Jess?' he asked. My tongue seemed to cleave to the roof of my mouth. I couldn't speak. 'I've been watching you, you know, from the mound up there.' He pointed to a rise to our right not far from his cottage. 'When I've been out feeding the pigs.' I knew the pigs were kept away from the cottage, especially in the summer and allowed to wander round the edge of the moor.

'I just wanted to ride her,' I replied feebly. 'I meant no harm.' Was this to be another thrashing from Aunt Anne? I just didn't care if it was, I would do the same again given the chance. My feet were now on the ground. I lifted my eyes to Mr McAndrew and looked at him. He was very tall. Six feet two to be exact.

'Please, Mr McAndrew, don't tell Aunt Anne.'

Down on the ground I wasn't so brave about the thrashing I would surely get if she knew. I looked up again. I think it must have been the first time I ever really saw his eyes, and what I saw I liked. He had eyes like Uncle Dunk, I thought, only not so deep set.

'Well,' he said slowly, as if pondering over a difficult problem. 'I need someone to take the horses to the moor all summer and bring them back when I need them. Nan is going away to Rothesay next week to live with her Aunt.'

My heart leapt with joy. Nan going away for ever. In my mind, people who left the Glen never came back. Joe Gardener, my knight in distress, had left a few months ago for Glasgow. So had Tom Madden. I was always afraid of Nan, for her sharp tongue constantly reminded me of who I was. If Mary wanted to play with me and Nan said no, that was that. If we were having a dispute, as children often do, and Nan was within hearing distance, she pounced, and my hair was pulled and my face slapped. 'Come on Mary, don't play with *her*.' The emphasis on the *her* was an insult in itself. I didn't dare retaliate for fear of further punishment, I just stood meekly by and let them go. I was awfully fond of Mary though and I knew she was of me too, so you can understand my joy at Nan's departure.

Mr McAndrew was still talking. 'Are you listening, Mina? I want you and Mary to take the horses to the moor grass. I'll see Anne about it. I would send Peter, but he is needed on the farm,' and with that he turned and left. I knew neither Bob nor Willie Whitelaw, the foster children, would be allowed to take them. To the McAndrews, riding horses just wasn't work, and the boys certainly had their share of that. Bob was ready to leave school in a few months' time which meant that, like all foster children, if he wasn't removed from his foster home, the farmer was allowed to keep him. Few, if any, of the foster children, ever stayed. They preferred to go to Glasgow or Edinburgh, according to the Authority to which they belonged.

Uncle Dunk was pleased when I told him what had happened. 'That's fine lass, isn't it Anne?'

Aunt Anne must already have been informed, as she showed

no surprise. 'As long as it doesn't interfere with her helping me. Anyhow, Andrew wants her to go with Mary.'

Andrew McAndrew's word seemed to be law in Balgreig. I noticed this on several other occasions. It was Andrew who said when the ploughing was to start, the seed to be sown, the hay gathered and the harvest. The potato lifting, the sheep shearing, the sheep dipping and clipping. Perhaps it was because his was the larger expanse of ground, and he certainly had the most livestock.

Chapter 5

How can I explain how I felt about the Glen?

When Mary and I went with Jess and Bute, McAndrew's horses, to the moor, a new beauty was laid out before me. On arrival at the moor, we saw in front and to the left of Tomnaloich, a velvet carpet of purple heather. The Lochan, an expanse of water stretching a quarter of a mile wide and a half mile long, reflected Tomnaloich in its calm peaceful waters. I couldn't drink in enough of this natural beauty.

The moor was fenced off by ditches running parallel with the fence or dyke, which kept the heather at bay, itself feeding a number of livestock belonging to Balgreig. Once the bridles were removed from the horses and the gate was opened, they galloped, neighing and bucking, to the small burn that sparkled its way to the lochan. On returning by the path we had come with the horses, Mary and I would sit by the loch chipping pebbles and watching the ripples wrinkling over the peaceful water. We became quite expert at skimming flat stones across the glassy surface. Pee-wees and lapwings cried above us. A lark sang its even song and gulls swooped and wheeled in the sky, eyeing all intruders. The eagle, king of birds, headed majestically towards its eyrie in the mountains, and the great stag stood sentinal on a rock, displaying his magnificent antlers against the blue of the sky and the purple of the mountains. All this and much, much more. I looked, saw, remembered and stored it all in my heart.

'Mary,' I said, 'in winter, we could come and skate here when the loch is frozen.'

'Oh, Mina, we would never be allowed. Would we?' She narrowed her eyes.

'I don't know, but I'm going to anyway,' I replied bravely.

Uncle Dunk always looked forward to me coming in from the moor. I would sit on my stool at his knee and talk of what we saw and did. 'You must have Highland blood in your veins, lass,' he would say when I told him of my feelings for Balgreig and its surroundings.

That year winter arrived early and the horses and sheep were brought in nearer to the village. The frost set in and the loch was frozen over. I took my skates from under the stair at the door and slipped out. It was a beautiful moonlit night. I was afraid to go to the loch alone and I stood looking about me. What should I do? Go on to the Lochan? Better not, I thought and turned to go back indoors when Willie Whitelaw approached from the McAndrew's cottage, his skates over his shoulder.

'Where do you think you're going?' he asked as he passed the gate at the bottom of our garden.

'And where do you think you're going, Willie?' answering question for question.

'To the Lochan,' was his reply. That did it. I opened the gate and joined him. 'So am I then.'

'You'll get a hammering,' he warned.

'So will you,' I retaliated.

'The McAndrews don't care as long as I'm in by 8 o'clock. They will think I am in the barn learning my lessons.'

Willie was clever in school. He could beat me to sticks and was nearly always at the top of his class, which didn't please the Glen folk. The foster children couldn't possibly beat their children, but when it came to brains, Willie Whitelaw showed them, and as I've said before our headmaster was very just. We passed the Fraser croft and young Andrew Fraser stepped out.

'That you Willie?' he shouted.

'Yes, Andrew.'

'Who have you got there?' Andrew asked curiously.

'It's me,' I replied, 'and I'm coming too.'

In five minutes or so we arrived at the lochan. There were no skating boots in those days. At least we had never heard of them. Our skates were strapped onto our boots. With the moon and stars above me and the ice below, I felt wonderful flying across the loch. I forgot there was another world beyond this patch of ice, another world where I would need to face the music when I returned. I seemed to go on and on, turn, sketch figure eights, and race away again to the furthest side of the loch. I didn't hear Andrew nor Willie shouting it was time to go. They had it timed to the minute and didn't get caught, but time meant nothing to me. It wasn't until I grew tired and headed back to the other side of the loch, that I realised what had happened.

Mr Fraser and Mr McAndrew were standing about fifty yards apart at another part of the loch. Aunt Anne was standing, with arms on hips, and in her hand as she approached the edge where I was heading, was a strap.

'Get them off,' she said, pointing to my skates. I unstrapped the skates from my boots. Where were Andrew and Willie I wondered? I didn't dare ask in case I would give them away, but they might have told me, I thought. No one spoke, but as I rose from the side of the loch with my skates in my hand, Aunt Anne strapped me over the legs, body, arms and face. There was no let up. I ran behind Mr Fraser, but he drew me back in front of Aunt Anne. 'Take your beating girl, you deserve it,' he shouted.

They are going to kill me, I thought, as Aunt Anne lashed me across the face again. I took to my heels and ran and ran. I got to the Brae House and flung open the door. 'Uncle Dunk, Uncle Dunk,' I sobbed. Then I stopped in my tracks. The kitchen was filled with women. There was Mrs McAndrew, Mrs McDonald, Mrs Fraser and Mrs McMillan. Their eyes were cold, their mouths stern and unsmiling. When I got to Uncle Dunk's chair, he wouldn't look at me. This was terrible.

'Uncle Dunk, don't be angry. I just had to to go the lochan and skate,' I blurted. He didn't even look up. The door was opened and Aunt Anne stepped in. 'Thank you all for coming,' she said, 'but its all right now. I'll deal with her.' The women started muttering among themselves.

'Ungrateful bissom, wicket brat. I'd get rid of her if I were you, Anne.' 'She is nothing but trouble,' someone else said. The door closed behind them.

'Get your clothes off, girl,' Aunt Anne ordered. I stared at her. 'Not in front of Uncle Dunk,' I said. I was now nine years old and felt I was no longer a small child. 'Get them off.' I could see what she wanted. My utter humiliation in front of Uncle Dunk. This woman hated me. Why? And if she did, why keep me in her house? Was it because I carried in the peat from the end of the house, drew the water from the well, ran errands, washed dishes, scrubbed floors, cleaned windows, and polished the oilcloth on the parlour floor? Sawed and chopped wood? I did all this because I wanted to help her and Uncle Dunk and because I looked on the Brae House as my home. I had taken thrashings before, but this was different.

'Upstairs I will strip and you can thrash me there,' I said

defiantly. I knew I could never do as she had asked. I turned to Uncle Dunk. 'Do you want me to take all my clothes off here and be thrashed?'

He looked at me for the first time since I came in. 'What you did was very wrong, Mina. I was worried. We all thought you were in the loch. Now, get upstairs to your bed.'

He spoke to Anne. 'She has had enough Anne, her face is bleeding. See to it.'

I was utterly exhausted. My body was all sore with the strap. Aunt Anne followed me up. 'Let me see your face. Hmph, its not bad enough. He saved your hide again, though why I listen to him I don't know. Wash yourself and get to bed.'

When she went downstairs, for the first time in my life at the Brae House I heard voices raised in anger. I didn't understand it all. Their Gaelic was slurred in anger and their voices sounded strange to my ears. I was not accustomed to hearing fighting between husband and wife. They were a couple of very few words. That night I cried myself to sleep.

The episode was never mentioned again, not even the following winter. Those who had skates were all allowed to skate over the loch under the supervision of Mr McAndrew, who turned out to all our surprise, to be a very good skater. When the thaw set in and the ice started to 'roor' as we called it, the skates were hung up for another season. But my whole attitude on life was to change before then. And the following winter turned out to be a mild one, so there was no skating on the loch.

Chapter 6

I was now eleven years old and the school holidays had arrived. Mary and I, with Betty Kelly, Mrs McDonald's foster girl, were approaching the village. We had been helping Betty's guardian with the hay ricks, helping to tie the ropes. This was done by pulling a bunch of hay from the bottom, twisting it into a rope which was then thrown over the rick to the other side and fastened the same way. Betty's sister, Florence, had left the village two weeks before, and, feeling very much alone, Betty started to join Mary and myself for company. We all helped each other at Balgreig with whatever job had to be done; we just set in and helped, providing we told our folks where we were going and were not required in the house. I had never

side-stepped the rules since that night on the loch, not because
of Aunt Anne, but because of Uncle Dunk, who had made me
promise never to go adventuring again without asking him first.
I never broke that promise.

As we were nearing Betty's house, her foster mother appeared
at the door.

'Your Aunt has visitors Mina, and you are wanted. Hurry
along now.'

I looked at Mary in surprise. 'Visitors?' I turned back to
Mrs McDonald. 'Thank you for telling. I am just going home
anyway.'

'Who will they be I wonder, Mary?'

'I don't know, unless its the authorities again.'

'But there's not a car to be seen,' I replied, as I made my way
across "the green" towards the Brae House. 'I'll see you later,
Mary. I'll go home now until the visitors have left.'

As I entered the kitchen, a woman was sitting beside Uncle
Dunk and a boy of my age was standing beside her. Aunt Anne
was laying the table.

'Push the sway over the fire,' she said, 'until the kettle comes
to the boil again.' I did as I was told.

Uncle Dunk held out his hand towards me. 'This is your
Aunt Anne's cousin and Donald, her boy. Mrs McKenzie has
come quite a distance and is waiting tea, so help Aunt Anne.'

I approached the table and busied myself with cups and
saucers, taking them from the dresser over to the table. I
noticed they were the second best set, so Mrs McKenzie,
although quite important, wasn't very important.

When tea was ready, Uncle Dunk took the head of the table.
I always helped him to the table by helping him to rise. I
twisted the chair round quickly, then waited for him until he
sat down. Aunt sat at the bottom, Mrs McKenzie and Donald
sat on Uncle's right and I on the opposite side. Uncle said grace.

I was sitting opposite Aunt's cousin, and managed to study
her. She was a large buxom woman with rosy cheeks, and thick
hair, just turning grey, which was swept severely from her face
and fastened in a bun on top of her head. Her eyes were grey
like Aunt's, but softer, her mouth fuller and sweeter. When she
smiled, she showed a mouthful of good teeth. Her son Donald
was a quiet sly-looking boy, not like his mother at all. The only
thing I noticed about him that he had inherited from her, was
the eyes, which were the same colour. He will have hard eyes
like Aunt when he is older, I thought, and immediately dismissed him from my mind. I don't think I liked him very much.

Aunt's cousin was talking. As yet, she hadn't spoken to me. 'Of course she can come Anne. Why not? Her bite will never be missed. I have six already, so what is another mouth?'

'Not two weeks, Meg, one will do,' said Uncle. It was then I realised they were talking about me. I was to go on holiday to some big farm about seven miles away.

'There is plenty to be done at home here.'

'Tchh, Anne. Let the lassie come for a week,' Mrs McKenzie argued. 'She will be well looked after and she can't get into mischief at Drumoich. It will also give you both a rest.'

I looked round at Uncle. I didn't know he wasn't keeping well. My stomach turned a little. Was his face thinner? I couldn't really tell as he had grown his beard longer lately. But I had noticed how he sometimes had difficulty in lifting his fork and using his knife. That surely didn't mean he was ill? I wished that I knew more about illness. Uncle saw me looking at him anxiously. 'Nonsense, Meg. I'm fine. My arms and legs are a wee bit stiff, that's all.'

Meg looked at me. 'We will see you then, Mina, at Drumoich next month. You will like it there,' she smiled. I wasn't very keen but with my true Highland manners, thanked her for her kindness. We both looked at each other across the table, smiling. I wonder what we would have said or done had we been able to see into the future.

When the dishes were cleared away, Meg decided to leave because they had a long hike home and wanted to be through the Plantation, a young forest, before dusk. She didn't seem to like that dark walk any more than I did. Aunt Anne placed her shawl over her shoulders. 'Wash the dishes, Mina, and don't break a cup mind. Then bring in the peat and some clogs. I will walk a bit of the road with you, Meg.'

Saying goodbye to Uncle and me, they left. I hadn't even spoken to Donald. That was the way of it in those days when children seldom spoke to each other in the presence of their elders.

Chapter 7

Aunt Anne was packing a clean shift in a valise and a change of dress and coat. I would have to go to church on Sunday, holiday or no holiday.

'When you get down to the school, stand at the main road and don't move! Charlie will come along with his bus and pick you up. Now be off with you. By the time you get down, you won't have long to wait. Just tell Charlie where you are going.'

I stood in the middle of the kitchen floor. Aunt had lifted my valise made of fine straw and handed it to me. 'Aunt Anne . . .' I said. What did I want to say? How could I say to this woman, what I wanted to say, whose roof gave me shelter. The words just stuck in my throat. Instead I turned to Uncle Dunk, threw my arms around his neck and kissed him. 'Goodbye Uncle.'

'Get on with you, lassie. You are only going away for a week,' he said quickly, but I saw that his eyes were moist. He would miss me as I would miss him. Aunt Anne tut-tutted. 'What a fuss.'

Uncle slipped something into my hand. 'Your Aunt forgot to give you the money for Charlie.' It was sixpence.

I didn't have to wait long. The small bus which held about fourteen people ground to a halt when I was spotted on the roadside.

'Jump in, lassie.' A man's voice spoke from the wheel. I stepped onto a bus for the first time.

'I am going to Drumoich,' I told the driver and held out my sixpence.

'Aye, Meg McKenzie told me to expect you. You will be Anne Gordon's girl, Mina Forbes.' I nodded. 'Take a seat,' said Charlie.

I still held out my sixpence. 'Put that in your pocket,' he said, his round smiling face beaming at me. 'I'll get it on the road back.'

The bus, Charlie's Henhouse, was square with wooden seats facing each other and mail bags piled at the back. It was the only convenience on the road carrying the mail and people going in to Inverness. He travelled every day except Sunday from Glen Affric to Inverness and back, stopping at Post Offices, farms and croft road ends delivering or receiving messages and errands. Few people up North travelled in those days, unless it was absolutely necessary. That day, there were three people in the bus and one little girl who sat on her mother's knee all the time I was there. I couldn't see out of the two small windows, which were one on each side of the bus, and I was too shy to get off my seat to see where I was going. The bus often stopped and started. Charlie would get out, and after a chat to someone come back, and off we went again. I was wondering if he had forgotten me, when the bus drew up and 'Right Mina,' he shouted. 'Here's where you get off.'

Picking up my valise, I stepped off the bus. 'Anyone meeting you?' Charlie asked. 'I don't know,' I replied.

'Oh well, it doesn't matter. See the road going up there.' He pointed with his finger. 'Follow it about a mile up, turn left, and you are there.' With a wave of his hand he was gone.

I followed his instructions. When I came to the cross-roads and was about to turn left, a young woman of about twenty approached. 'Are you Mina?'

I replied that I was. She took my valise. 'Charlie is surely early. I meant to be further down. Oh, my name is Meg.'

I could see at a glance she was very like her mother and I could imagine her mother looking just like this when she was young with dark hair and laughing eyes. Meg was slim enough just now, but later she would be buxom like her mother.

Drumoich was a large farm house with front and back doors, something I had never seen before. The kitchen was large and airy and Meg called it the 'scullery'. I had never heard of that before either. All the cooking was done in the scullery on a range, which was also new to me and had to be cleaned with black lead until the steel parts gleamed. The table, larger than Aunt Anne's, was scrubbed white. The kitchen was a place to sit in after the day's work was finished. A large Damask cloth was spread over a table in the centre of the floor and a sofa and horsehair chairs were round the table. I stood timidly beside one of the chairs.

Meg McKenzie was combing the fair curly hair of a little girl of about three. 'Hello Mina,' she said, as she drew a blue silk ribbon from her mouth and started binding a bunch of the fair hair. 'Glad you could come. Just make yourself at home now, dinner will be ready in five minutes. Young Meg will show you where to wash your hands. This is our baby, Jean,' she continued nodding towards the small child. 'Run along pet, and tell Alex to come. He is out the back with his rabbits.'

I went with Meg to the scullery, took off my coat and started to wash my hands at a basin set on a small marble stand near the door. 'Just throw the water down the drain at the back door when you are finished,' Meg instructed. 'I will hang up your coat and put your valise in my room. And you will sleep with me.'

I did as I was told. As I turned to come in, after getting rid of the water, a boy of about eight approached with Jean. He was fair like his sister. 'I'm Alex,' he said and ran past me into the house. Donald, the brother who had come to Aunt Anne's with his mother, came in a few minutes later. We looked at each other. I smiled. 'Hello,' I said timidly. He nodded.

Young Meg returned from another part of the house, calling orders to the children, and stood beside her mother who was already dishing up the dinner.

'John,' she called to a young boy of about fourteen, 'get them round the table before your father comes in.' John, tall for his age, was dark like his sister Meg. He took one look at me and to Donald.

'I see your girl-friend has arrived.'

Poor Donald blushed to the roots of his hair. 'She's not my girl-friend. I hate her.'

His mother came into the kitchen. 'Donald, do you want a smacking? Go and stand at your place.'

She then turned to me. 'He spoke a lot about you to Alex when he came back from Anne's. Now you stand here beside John.'

Does everyone stand to eat in this house? What's all the chairs for then, I thought, nearly giggling. I soon knew the reason. A voice, loud and clear came through the scullery door. 'Dinner ready, Meg? I'm starving. Everyone in?'

'Everyone, except Craig,' Meg answered.

'He's here,' replied the voice, 'just washing his hands at the spout.'

Young Meg then brought the soup to the table in a large tureen. Her mother entered, took her place at the bottom of the table where the tureen had been placed. Behind her, a very tall man, as tall as Mr McAndrew, but much broader entered. Immediately there was silence from the children, even little Jean stopped prattling. Mr McKenzie took his place at the top of the table and nodded his head. All the children sat down silently on the chairs in front of them, except Jean, who was lifted by young Meg onto a high chair beside her mother. Only then did Mr McKenzie look at me.

'Sit down, lass and make yourself at home,' he said warmly. 'We don't have any foster children in this family. You are one of us as long as you are here. Where is Craig?' he asked Meg. 'I am about to say Grace.'

'I'm here, Dad.' A youth of eighteen entered the kitchen and took his place at the table at his father's right hand. I didn't look at him until Grace was said.

When I lifted my eyes, he was staring at me across the table. His dark wide-set eyes met mine. Dark curly hair topped a firm strong face and a half smile curled the corner of his mouth. His body was the body of an athlete. I don't think I had ever seen anyone so good looking before. This knowledge didn't come to me then, but years later. For the present, I liked what I saw and what he said.

'So—you are Mina. My, but you are a beauty, isn't she Donald?' he said to his brother.

'She's not,' Donald said, blushing again.

'But she is,' Craig replied, 'you will break a few hearts in a few years, Mina, I'll bet.'

'Oh stop tormenting Donald,' Meg said, 'and leave Mina alone.'

I felt as if I was singing inside and felt happy as I had never done before. I felt wanted and loved as I had always wanted to be loved. Uncle Dunk's love for me was protective and comforting, but this was different. I don't know how to explain it. I only knew that as I looked at Craig once more and saw the admiration in his eyes, I responded to it. I was only eleven, but I instantly knew that Craig McKenzie was to play a big part in my life. What it was to be I had no idea. I just knew.

Immediately after dinner, everyone except baby Jean, went about their chores, As Craig passed me he gave my hair a gentle pull. 'See you, beautiful,' he said and passed out of doors.

'If you want to help,' Mrs McKenzie said, 'go and put on your pinny and help Meg with the dishes. Tomorrow is Sunday and there is a lot to do.'

There certainly was. Mrs McKenzie never seemed to stop. Food was cooked, water was brought in, and peat and logs by the boys. Clothes were looked out and examined for the Sabbath. A missing button, a sock or stocking with the tiniest hole didn't escape the eye of mother. After supper, which was served in the kitchen about seven o'clock, the boys went into the scullery. A zinc bath sat in the middle of the floor and Meg and her mother set to washing the boys and Jean. The older boys went outside stripped to the waist, and washed at the big barrel at the gable of the house. This was rain water that dropped from the rone pipe into the barrel. They scooped the water out into a large bath, which sat on a wooden bench, father included. Meg, her mother and I all washed in our own rooms, then emptied the water, wiped the enamelled basin and returned it to the marble stand for further use.

Next morning, we all rose about eight o'clock, washed and went down to prayers. After breakfast, we dressed for best, and the trap was brought round, the horse saddled up and we were ready.

The church was not the same one as the people of Balgreig attended, 'The Wee Free'. The church we were going to was the 'United Free'. Two very different churches. The ministers preached on the same theme, sackcloth and ashes and 'where would we spent eternity,' etc. But in the United Church, there was an organ and a choir. I enjoyed it very much, especially as I was sitting beside Craig.

As we entered the church, Craig came to my side. 'Follow me,' he whispered. Meg and her mother entered the seat first with Jean between them, followed by Alex, then Donald. John stepped aside for me to pass, but Craig indicated to him to sit down. I followed John, then Craig took his seat, with his father bringing up the rear. We didn't look at each other, nor did he share his hymn book with me. I shared John's. But I was perfectly happy and content just to sit beside him.

When we arrived home, the horse was unsaddled and turned into the paddock behind the house. Dinner was cold and without potatoes. After the dishes were cleared, our Sunday clothes were put away and second best put on. I thought it would be the same as at home. Bible reading. This was not so.

The children disappeared somewhere into the farm steading. Jean was lying sucking her thumb on the sofa with a rug wrapped round her, ready for her nap. Mr and Mrs McKenzie were settling down to a quiet afternoon chat. Meg, I was told, was going to see her future mother-in-law. She was engaged to a farmer's son further up the Glen.

I was sitting on the sofa when Craig came downstairs. 'I understand you can ride, Mina,' he said. I nodded. 'Come on then we will have a trot.'

'Not on a Sunday, surely, Craig?' his mother said.

'Why not, Mum, we won't leave the farm, so who will see us?'

'John,' she said, addressing his father, 'do you hear what he is wanting to do?'

'Let him go,' Mr McKenzie replied. 'He works hard all week. Let him show our guest this part of the Glen. I'm sure she will find it just as beautiful as Balgreig.' I doubted this very much, but was too well mannered to say so.

We arrived at the paddock where two hill ponies were grazing. Donald appeared at the stable door. Bring out two bridles and two saddles for the ponies, Donald, please,' Craig said and he walked over to the ponies and caught one by its mane. Donald appeared again and I went to help him. 'I wish you had never come here,' he said bitterly. 'If you are to be with Craig all the time.'

Before I could answer, he walked past me to the pony I was to ride, laid down the bridle and saddle on the ground and ran back to the stables. I wasn't tall enough to saddle Queenie, so I left it to Craig. When we had mounted, Craig turned. 'Have you ever seen Loch Ness, Mina?' he said. I shook my head.

'I know where it is. We get it in geography at school,' I answered.

In order to see it to advantage from the farm, we had to climb up the crags about half a mile above the farm and look across. What a view met my eyes. To my right and far to the west was the great forest.

'We must be higher up here than at Balgreig,' I said. 'We can only see part of the forest from there. I didn't realise it was so big.'

I could see he was watching me intently. The loch was about two miles distant below us and it was beautiful. Across the loch, Urquhart Castle loomed up. 'I wonder who lived there in days gone by? Were they happy and were they worthy of their heritage?' I wasn't aware I had spoken aloud until Craig said, 'You like the Glen, Mina?'

'Oh, yes, Craig, I love it,' I breathed. 'I never want to leave it.'

He helped me down from Queenie and took my hand. 'We will leave the ponies here. I have something else to show you.' I was loath to turn my back on the loch. 'Come,' he said, 'You will see it again in a little while.'

We climbed up the crags to their pinnacle. 'What do you think of that,' Craig said proudly. It was a vast expanse of moor, mountain and forest with a loch dotted here and there at the foot of the mountains. The clouds overhead cast shadows below. It was absolutely desolate, but its splendour was breathtaking. Craig spoke very quietly. 'Mina, beyond all that is the Black Isle,' he said with a sweep of his arm. 'My Uncle has a farm like my father's over there. The Black Isle is beautiful too. Come, let's go back.'

We returned to the ponies which were wandering about aimlessly and mounted again. For a long time I stared at it all, drinking in the beauty of the loch and the castle and the curve of the road leading from Lewiston to Fort Augustus.

We rode in silence down to the farm. There was no reason for speech between us. It seemed to me as if I had known Craig all my life. Although he was seven years older than me, it didn't seem to matter one iota.

The rest of the week was like the first twenty four hours, happy, contented, and never to be forgotten. If Uncle Dunk could also live here in this house of love, my heaven on earth would have been complete. But this was not heaven and I had to return. After a tearful leave of my new friends, Meg took me down to the bus. 'We will see that you get back. Oh here's Charlie.'

'Goodbye,' I said and entered the bus, handing Charlie my sixpence. 'Had a nice week?' he asked in his cheerful way. 'Here's your tuppence change now.' I nodded and sat in the first seat I came to.

I arrived home that night about seven o'clock. Uncle Dunk and I were glad to see each other and I could see that he had missed me. For all my happiness at Drumoich, I had missed him too. All Aunt Anne had to say, after asking after her cousin, was, 'Well, early to bed, my girl. I'm washing blankets tomorrow and I'll need you to tramp them.'

Chapter 8

Never a day passed without me thinking of Craig. Although we were only seven miles apart, we might have been separated by the seven oceans of the world because in those days people didn't go far out of their villages and a radius of seven miles was quite a bit. Anyone who went into Inverness for a day was looked on with awe and respect. They had travelled into a big city and seen sights we never dreamt of.

When I returned to school in September, we had a new headmaster, Mr Nicholl, a much younger teacher whose methods were different. He taught us about the world outside and what to expect. He spoke of electricity and gas in the towns. He told us about running water in homes. He explained how all this came about. The boys looked on him as a hero and listened eagerly, their mouths wide open and their eyes full of wonder. We girls got bored with the explanations of how electricity worked, how the water rose to the tap, and how gas was made. I felt that he was preparing the boys for the outside world and not bothering about us.

I complained to Uncle Dunk about this. 'You listen lassie,' he said, 'it will affect you too.'

'Affect me Uncle, how?'

'You are going on for twelve and you sit your Qualifying Exam next May,' he explained. 'In less than two years you will be away.'

I stood staring at him. Me—going from the Glen, never. What rubbish. 'Uncle Dunk, you can't mean that,' I said. He looked up from his chair. 'Mina, the Glen will never hold you. I've been watching you this while back, ever since you came home from Drumoich. You are restless, nor do you play so much with childish things. Take the other day for instance. When Anne and I thought you were out with Mary and the other children, you went to the moor, round the Loch and climbed to the gulls' nest on the crags. And by yourself.'

I didn't answer, but what Uncle said was true. I didn't want to play so much. More and more I wanted to be alone, but I wasn't alone. I felt Craig's presence and I wondered if he was thinking of me. Was I just fascinated by him or was it a sort of hero worship children sometimes have for an older person. I just didn't know. 'Uncle Dunk.' I sat down beside him on my stool. 'I'm awfully fond of Craig McKenzie. Oh I like all the family, but Craig is special.'

For a long time there was silence. When he spoke, his voice was quiet and gentle. 'Keep your sights a little lower, lass,' his voice was almost a whisper, 'that way, you won't get hurt.'

I didn't quite understand his meaning and thought perhaps he hadn't heard me right. Years later I was to remember his words.

Chapter 9

I passed my Qualifying Exam which entitled me to go on for further education, but Aunt Anne thought it better to finish my schooling where I was, at the age of fourteen.

Uncle Dunk took to his bed on Sunday. On Monday morning I went in to help him with his jacket and socks as I had done down through the years. Aunt Anne put his trousers on and I did the rest. He was usually sitting on the edge of the bed waiting for me, but this morning, he was just lying there. 'I can't move my legs, Mina,' he said, his voice wavering. 'Get Anne.' I ran to the henhouse where Aunt Anne was letting out the hens. 'Uncle can't move his legs,' I gasped.

'I know,' said Aunt Anne, 'I've asked Mr McAndrew to go to Drumm for the doctor. He is taking the trap, so he will take you all down to school. Your "piece" is lying on the dresser. Pick it up on the way out.' All this was said in a calm, clear voice.

I stared at her. Had this woman no feeling for her man? I know she didn't love me. I had discovered that many years ago. But her man. 'How did you know?' I asked feebly.

'I saw him through the door trying to move his legs when I was making the breakfast.' Again this came in a voice that had no trace of feeling. 'You'd better hurry.'

The tears were blinding me as I made my way back indoors. I couldn't let Uncle see me like this. 'I've got to go,' I called through the door to him. 'Aunt Anne is here.' I swept past her, my 'piece' in my hand.

Uncle was never to walk again, which meant he required much more attention, and on that account when Aunt Anne said I wasn't to go to High School, I made no fuss.

It meant I could help her to make Uncle more comfortable and also do the housework and the washing. I thought that this would just go on in the same way, even when I left school.

It was two years later that the bombshell fell. Our Easter holidays started on the Thursday. I arrived home and made for Uncle Dunk's room.

'Well, that's school finished for a fortnight Uncle.' I said. 'Mary and I are going to keep our promise to you tomorrow, if it is nice. Aunt is going to dress you and then Mary and I are going to lift you on to your chair with the help of her Dad and Peter.' This was a secret Mary and I had kept from him. He was only to be told on the first day of our holidays.

I waited for the old twinkle to come into his eyes, but it didn't. 'A letter came today, Mina,' he said. 'Anne has it.'

'A letter?' I asked puzzled; then I felt something cold inside me. 'What letter?' There was no answer. He lifted his eyes to the ceiling. My room was above.

'Upstairs, sorting out your things,' his voice was thick with emotion.

I ran up the dozen steps to the attic bedroom and barged in. 'What letter came today, and what are you doing?' My voice shook with fear. Without a word, she handed me the letter from her apron pocket.

I can't remember it word for word, but it was from a Mrs Gray and she wanted me to catch the 11 o'clock train from Inverness to Edinburgh on 2nd April, nine days from the date it was written. I would be met by the under-chauffeur and taken to the home of the Earl and Countess of Inverleith, to work as a fifth housemaid.

'Who arranged this?' I asked, thinking of the Authorities. Aunt Anne took the letter back, folded it and carefully put it back into her apron pocket.

'I did. I knew Mrs Gray thirty years ago. We worked together. She is now housekeeper at Inverleith Hall and she is engaging you because of past acquaintance.'

'Who wrote to her then?' I asked. Not Aunt Anne, she couldn't write English.

'Mrs McAndrew did,' she said triumphantly. That bitch! I might have known.

'And the Authorities in Aberdeen, do they know?'

'Oh yes, we have attended to everything. They are quite agreeable,' she said.

Letters must have been passed to and fro. Aunt Anne must have read my thoughts. 'You are supposed to be that clever but that's something you didn't know, eh?'

'I am going to Drumoich to Mrs McKenzie, she will have me,' I said hurriedly. I must see Craig, I thought. He will never let me leave the Glen. These people loved me, they treated me like their own kin. I grabbed my coat from behind the door and ran downstairs to Uncle Dunk. 'Don't worry Uncle, I'm going to Drumoich. I'll be back.'

I took a short cut. To go all the way round the road was seven miles, not including the two from Balgreig to the school where I got the bus. I had been to Drumoich twice since my first visit, on both occasions missing Craig, who was over at the Black Isle at his Uncle's farm. I made my way across the moor to the Plantation which held no fear for me on this day, meeting the main road four miles further on and cutting out more than two miles. My feet had wings.

When I arrived at Drumoich farm, John and Donald were driving the cows out to the grazing paddock. They saw me from the distance and waved. 'Back again?' John shouted and little Jean ran out of the house and embraced me. She was seven years old now and a very pretty girl. As I bent down to receive her embrace I asked, 'Where's Craig?'

'At the blacksmith's with Big Boy,' was the answer. Big Boy was one of the Clydesdales. I felt my anger and fear drop from me. He was here, everything was good. I entered the well-loved kitchen. 'Hello everyone.' I said.

Meg and John McKenzie were standing at the fireside talking. Alex came through from the scullery drying his hands. 'Welcome for Easter,' Meg said in her usual cheerful way. 'I'm surprised Anne allowed you. She must be getting mellow in her old age.'

'She isn't staying Meg, by the look of things,' John McKenzie said. She hasn't got her Sunday clothes with her, so she will be going home before Sabbath.'

I turned to Meg. 'I must speak to you. I . . .'

'Now, now, you are tired, Mina. We'll all have supper first. I'm sure you must be hungry, walking from Balgreig. John, go out and get the boys in.' Turning again to me, she said 'Take off your coat, Mina, and help with the table. You know where everything is.'

'That must be Craig back,' Jean said, 'I hear Big Boy's hooves in the yard.'

My heart sang and it seemed an age before the kitchen door opened. Although my back was to the door, I knew he was there and turned.

'Why, Mina, hallo!' His whole face lit up and his eyes glowed. 'My but you have grown.' His eyes wandered from my face to the rest of my body. I felt shy and awkward, like the schoolgirl I was. This wasn't at all the youth I had last seen. Here was a man. His voice was deeper than I had known and he was broader and taller.

I spoke little at the table and noticed that Craig was also very quiet. but the rest of the family made up for it. I thought that perhaps Craig was now too grown up to join in their prattle. Young Meg was missing. She had married six months earlier. I wasn't at the wedding, but Aunt Anne had gone, while I stayed behind and kept Uncle Dunk company.

After the dishes were cleared away, I helped with the washing up. The boys were going in and out, taking in peat and wood. Craig and his father were discussing the work that had been done on the farm that day. John was also included in the discussion. After all, he was now sixteen. It wasn't until the two younger children were sent to bed that Meg turned to me. 'Now Mina, what's the matter?'

I told the company everything that had happened, not in anger and fear, but quietly and precisely. No one spoke for a few moments, then John McKenzie got up, stood with his back to the fire and lit his pipe.

'I'm sorry, Mina, but you can't stay here. I would never be allowed to have you supposing I wanted to, and I don't. Craig,' he said, 'you will write to Duncan and Anne telling them we are sorry if we have caused them any trouble keeping Mina here tonight. She can't go home now, its dark.'

My face drained of all its colour and a great lump rose in my throat, choking back any words. I couldn't speak. From a distance I heard Meg's voice saying 'John is right, Mina. That sounds like a very nice place where you are going, and it was very good of Anne to go to all the trouble to get you settled. After all, the Authorities could have taken you back to Aberdeen and shoved you into service there, not nearly so good. Being fostered out isn't the same as being born in the Glen,' she finished.

John McKenzie put his hand gently on my arm. 'You will come and see us all here when you come up from Edinburgh. Cheer up, lass, its not the end of the world.'

He turned to Craig. 'Are you stuck to that chair, boy? I told you to write me a letter for Anne Gordon. Do it now. You will be out in the fields with John and I when she leaves in the morning.'

Craig rose and faced his father. 'If Mina doesn't want to leave the Glen, why should she? There are surely places she can go to service here, among people she knows. What kind of guardian has Anne Gordon been to her anyway? And why should you write and apologise to her?'

There was a terrible silence. John McKenzie's face turned very red. 'Are you speaking to me, boy?' he roared. Meg jumped in between them.

'There is no need for you to get upset, John. I'm surprised at you, Craig, speaking to your father like that, and over a slip of a girl too.'

I rose with the tears streaming down my cheeks as I groped for the coat I had left on the back of a chair. It wasn't there. Dear God, I thought, these people were my friends. They're not the people I knew, the people whom I thought loved me, who gave me the run of their home. I must be stupid. And I turned to Craig who was still glaring at his father.

'It's all right, Craig,' I whispered, 'please don't fight with your parents over me. Goodbye.' I made for the door. Meg McKenzie ran after me. 'You're not going home in the dark. Anyway, its nearly nine o'clock. You go to bed and I'll see you in the morning. You know your room,' she said patting my hand. 'Come on now, Mina, be a good girl, and go to bed.'

I looked at her as if she were a stranger thinking how tired I was. Yes, perhaps that would be best. 'It would upset Uncle Dunk if I walked into the house at midnight,' I said quietly. Wearily I climbed the stairs, but no sleep came to me that night. I heard the grandfather clock in the kitchen strike five o'clock, then half past five. I rose, splashed my face with cold water that I poured from the ewer into the basin. I dressed quickly, then combed my silky black hair and gazed into the mirror. What was the matter with me? They called me orphan and pauper, but I was no different from anyone else. I had a pretty face, round and well shaped. My eyes were hazel and set well apart. I was tall and my figure, although not yet fully rounded, would be one day.

I turned from the mirror. My coat was hanging at the back of the door. It must have been put there when we tidied up after supper. I slipped quietly out with my boots in my hand, opened the front door, shut it gently and turned to go. It was then I saw him. Craig was waiting at the gable of the house. 'What are you doing here?' I asked.

'Oh I heard you get up. You sleep next door to me, you know.'

'I didn't sleep a wink, Craig,' I said.

'Neither did I,' he replied.

'Never mind, Mina. You wait. One day I'll be my own boss. Keep yourself for me, Mina.'

I looked at Craig's earnest face. 'Keep myself for you, Craig?' I said puzzled. My heart leapt in my breast. Instead of answering me, he drew me to him and kissed me on the cheek, then turned and quickly walked away. Did Craig mean what he said, or was he sorry for me and only trying to make the blow I had received from his parents a little easier? Time was to tell.

I arrived home just before nine o'clock. Aunt Anne had gone to church, as most of the village had, it being Easter Friday. I made straight for Uncle Dunk's room. When I saw this poor crippled creature, I knew that he was the only person I could bare my soul to, and I did. I knelt on the rug beside his bed. My head lay on the counterpane, my two hands gripped one of his and then the flood gates opened and I sobbed as if my heart would break. How long I wept, I don't know. I only know that when I finally lifted my head, there was Uncle Dunk smiling tenderly. I told him everything, including my love for Craig.

'Mina, lass,' he said, 'your love is a child's love, not a woman's. It won't last. I'm sure when you come home again, you will be telling me all about your conquests with boys of your own age. After all,' he reminded me, 'Craig is seven years older than you. It's hero worship, not love. You have that to know yet.' Poor Uncle Dunk, how wrong he was.

On 2nd April, I was ready. Mr McAndrew was taking me to Charlie's bus with my trunk. I didn't say goodbye to Uncle that morning. I couldn't. I had written him a note and slipped it under his pillow when I said goodnight the evening before with words of thanks that I couldn't say to his face. As I made for the door, Aunt Anne was standing there. She held out her hand. I ignored it, but looked straight at her. My gaze was cold and calculating. Our eyes met. Her eyes were the first to drop, and I walked out.

Chapter 10

What can I say about 'service' that hasn't been all said before especially in large homes and castles. It was hard work. Up early. Time off for meals. Only one half day per week. And Sunday free to go to church. I wasn't unhappy though. I was well fed and the housekeeper left me entirely to the Head Housemaid, Kate.

Kate was kind to me, but at the same time saw to it I did my work properly. My duties consisted of keeping the staff quarters clean, the Housekeeper's and the butler's, the Head Housemaid's, Ladies Maid's and Footman's and Steward's room. As the last housemaid of five, I was the lowest paid. Five shillings a week. The only time I saw her Ladyship, The Countess of Inverleith, was on Christmas Eve, when the whole staff, about twenty, collected in the Billiard Room to receive our Christmas presents.

By the time it was my turn, there were only two left, mine and the Scullery Maid's. I found her ladyship very charming and beautiful. She asked me my name, age and where I came from, then handed me an umbrella, and a handbag to Elsie, the Scullery Maid. We curtsied, as we were told, and walked out, taking one step backwards before turning to the door.

In my bedroom, which I shared with Agnes, the fourth housemaid, I examined my umbrella. It was the first I'd ever had. As I looked at it I thought to myself, why should this tall gracious lady, The Countess of Inverleith, have so much and her staff so little? All the staff presents put together must have cost more money than I had ever dreamt of. Kate entered my room at that moment.

'Come, Mina,' she said, 'it's time you set the tea in the housemaids' sitting room.' This was the only meal the housemaids didn't have to take in the staff hall. 'You have also the Butler's tea to take to his office and Mrs Gray is having her tea in her sitting room with Miss Hood, the Ladies' Maid. Hurry now, girl.'

Something in me rebelled. 'Why should I scivvy to you all. I hate it and I hate you for making me do it.' A sob came into my voice as I said, 'All I ever wanted was to stay in the Glen. I never wanted to come here. I was made to . . . I . . .,' and my voice trailed away into silence.

Kate spoke quietly. 'I could report you for this to Mrs Gray, you know, and you would be instantly dismissed for insubordination, but because of your age and inexperience I'm going to overlook this outburst. But if it is ever repeated, I will not be so lenient.'

That was the first and last time I spoke like that to Kate. I discovered you couldn't fight the System and I was learning the hard way. To be dismissed instantly, or even given a month's notice, meant no references. If a reference was given grudgingly, it certainly stated the reason for dismissal in full detail. This was 1926. We were entering the depression and servants were 'two a penny' as the saying went, so I bowed to the inevitable and joined the System.

I wrote home every week to Uncle Dunk. I knew he couldn't write, but Mrs Fraser promised to drop me a note now and then and let me know how he was. This she did and I was most grateful. I never wrote to the McKenzies, nor did I ever receive a letter from Craig. I tried to shut Craig from my mind, but scarcely a day passed but I thought of him. Was it just hero-worship, as Uncle Dunk said, or was it possible for one so young to fall in love? It didn't seem to be so with Craig, or I would have had a letter from him. He knew where I was. Put him out of your mind, Mina Forbes, I told myself angrily, you are a fool. But I couldn't.

Chapter 11

I was fifteen and my holidays were only two weeks away. I would see the Glen, Uncle Dunk and Craig again. My spirits soared. I did my work with greater pleasure. I would have done anything just to please Kate and make her happy too. I wanted everyone to be happy, it was a wonderful feeling.

Then the letter came. It was written by Mrs McAndrew for Aunt Anne. Aunt Anne, it seemed, had some relation in Strathpeffer who had just died and left Aunt the contents of her home. I had heard about this cousin from Mrs McKenzie, but had forgotten all about her. The letter said that Aunt Anne had gone to Strathpeffer to see a lawyer, leaving Uncle Dunk with Mrs McAndrew. They had made a makeshift stretcher and taken him to her home. Aunt Anne was very sorry, but she couldn't have me for my week's holiday and Mrs McAndrew would have plenty to do looking after Uncle Dunk. I read the letter through a blur of tears. I had looked forward to this holiday so much that I just couldn't take it in.

I went to Kate and handed her the letter. She was sitting in the Housemaids' sitting room, sewing. She put her materials down and took the letter.

'What's this?' she asked. But glancing at my face, she knew. I couldn't answer.

Kate folded my letter and put it into its envelope. 'I am sorry,' she said quietly. 'Isn't there someone else who would take you?'

'I know Mrs Fraser would take me, but it would mean someone would be inconvenienced by her doing so.' I shook my head. 'No, there is no one who can take me.'

'You are a very proud girl, Mina,' Kate said, 'and I'm afraid it is going to make you very unhappy as you go through life.'

Finally, I spent my first holiday working. I didn't have to, but what was the point of wandering about the Estate grounds or going into Edinburgh. My disappointment was awful.

I suppose I could have gone up to the Glen. Someone would have put me up and I could have seen Uncle Dunk, but I didn't. I don't know why. It had to be, I suppose. Fate if you like.

Nine months later the telegram arrived. I was making the Housekeeper's bed, prior to cleaning the room. Jean, the second housemaid, popped her head round the door. 'You are wanted in the Housemaids' sitting room.' she said and disappeared.

'Bother,' I said aloud, 'What's wrong now?' Everything was timed in such a manner that the house ran like clockwork, even five minutes away from routine meant extra effort to bring the work up to scratch.

The Housekeeper and Head Housemaid were standing at the fireplace. A telegram had been opened by the Butler. 'When did you last hear from the Glen, Mina?' asked Mrs Gray.

'Last week,' I said.

'Who wrote to you?'

'Mrs Fraser.'

I knew the telegram was for me. I stepped forward. 'Give it to me please.' It was brief, as all telegrams are. *Come home. Duncan very ill*. Signed *Fraser*.

'When can I go, Mrs Gray?' I asked.

'Well it's not as if it is your father or even a relation. I really can't let you go without her Ladyship's permission.' Mrs Gray spoke gently but firmly.

'Please, Mrs Gray, ask her Ladyship. Please.' She looked at me. 'All right, Mina, but don't go building up your hopes.'

I nodded and Mrs Gray left. 'I'll get on with my work until Mrs Gray comes back, Kate,' I said and left the sitting room. I had no intention of going back to work. I was going to my room to pack a bag. I was returning to the Glen to Uncle Dunk, and no one was going to stop me. Ten minutes later, Kate called along the corridor.

'Mina, you are wanted.' I came out of my room. Kate didn't ask what I was doing in my room, when I should have been two corridors away. I followed her in silence to the Butler's Pantry. 'Here she is, Mr Connacher.' The Butler nodded. 'Follow me.'

I hadn't been in the front of the house, as we called the public rooms, since Christmas Eve to receive my annual present. We entered the gallery and arrived at her Ladyship's boudoir. 'Wait here,' the Butler indicated with his finger. He entered, spoke a few words and beckoned me in. 'Mina Forbes, the fifth housemaid, My Lady.'

The Butler shut the door quietly and I was alone with the Countess of Inverleith. She was writing at a beautiful Sheridan table and, as the door closed, she laid down her pen and turned. She lifted the telegram and spoke quietly. 'Good morning, Mina.'

'Good morning, My Lady,' I curtsied.

'Who is this person, Fraser, who has sent this telegram and who is Duncan? I see he is ill.' I told her and as she listened to me she watched me closely. 'What I don't understand,' she said at last, 'is why Mrs Gordon, your Guardian, hasn't sent for you.'

'My Lady,' I became bold. 'Duncan is the only father I've ever known.'

'I asked about your guardian, Mrs Gordon, Mina.'

'She can't write English,' I blurted out. I couldn't tell this beautiful lady how I was brought up. I couldn't tell her of the many, many small cruelties that were inflicted on me by Anne Gordon, nor could I tell her of the thrashings I had received from her hands on the smallest pretext. She would never have understood. I knew that by looking at her.

'Well,' she said finally. 'You didn't take a holiday last year, so you can have it now. Return here one week from today. See the Butler about getting transport to Edinburgh.'

I curtsied and withdrew. It was the first time Anne Gordon had done me a good turn, by telling Mrs McAndrew to write that I couldn't visit the Glen, as she was going to Strathpeffer.

All the way up from Edinburgh's Waverley Station to Inverness, I kept saying 'Don't let him die until I get there. Please God, don't let him die.'

When I arrived at Inverness, it was nine o'clock at night. I didn't know the town at all. I didn't know where to get Charlie's bus and, even if I did, it wouldn't be there at this time of night. I stood in the middle of the station when a porter approached. 'Can I help you, lass?'

'I have to get to the Glen somehow. My Uncle Dunk is ill.' He stood for a moment or two, then lifting my bag he said, 'Come with me.'

We entered a room full of porters. 'This young lady wants to get to the Glen,' he said.

'Which part?' asked one of the men.

'Balgreig,' I answered.

'What—Balgreig. That's twenty miles away and half-way up the mountains.' He laughed and was joined by one or two of his companions.

'I must get up,' I said frantically.

'Now, now lass,' said the porter who had brought me in, 'some of the lads have wives who will put you up for the night. It often happens. What about you, John?' He turned to a man in his late forties.

He rose. 'Certainly. My name is McIntosh. I'll take you home with me. I'm just going off duty. Goodnight all, see you tomorrow. Come on, lass.' He lifted my bag.

In those days, we had great trust in people, especially in the Highlands. It never entered my head that I didn't know this man, nor did I hesitate to go with him. It was quite natural. Today, it seems incredible, and just would not happen. But then, it was different. I was a girl from the Glen and I was needing help. I was offered help and accepted. Such was the way of the Highlander.

Mr McIntosh took me to Tomnahurich Street where he lived with his wife, Kirstie. He explained my presence and introduced us. 'Well come on then, and don't stand at the door,' Mrs McIntosh said.

I was fed with the hospitality of the Highlands, then shown to a small room at the back of the house and told, 'You will be tired, so just blow out the candle when you get into bed. Goodnight.' After praying that God would spare Uncle Dunk until I got home, I fell asleep.

In the morning, after my breakfast of oatmeal porridge and bannocks, I rose and took my leave. I offered Mrs McIntosh money which she refused. 'I'll tell you what,' she said, 'you come back and see me sometime and tell me all about yourself. I think it would be quite interesting.' I thanked her warmly and promised I would, and I did. But that is another story.

I got McBrayne's bus up to the Glen. It took the mail and left at nine o'clock. I asked the driver, whom I didn't know, about Charlie and his bus.

'Oh, Charlie has retired,' was the reply. 'McBrayne has taken over his run. I'm the driver, Bob Spilling.'

I stepped out of the bus at Dalreigh and there was my old school, but there were no children about. As it wasn't play-time or lunch, classes would probably be sitting. I walked the two and a half miles to Balgreig, lugging my bag. I got a wave from a few of the crofters who knew me. I wanted to stop and ask them about Uncle Dunk, but I thought better of it.

I arrived at the Brae House about noon. The door was slightly ajar, although the March wind was ice-cold. I pushed it open and walked into the kitchen. Aunt Anne was bending over the fire, arranging the peat. She didn't hear me enter. It wasn't until she had pushed the sway back over the fire, that she turned round. Her hand flew to her breast. 'Mina—I didn't hear you come in.'

I put down my case and went over beside her. 'How is Uncle?' I tried to keep my voice steady and hoped I was succeeding.

'He is still here.' Her voice was as calm as mine, but her eyes were very wary. She hadn't changed a bit except that perhaps her hair was whiter, if that was possible.

I removed my gloves, hat, and coat, laid them on Uncle Dunk's chair and went into his room. He was lying propped up with pillows as I had seen him so often before, but there was a great change in him. His eyes had sunken into the back of his head, his face was grey, and he seemed to me to have become an old, old man. I knelt down beside his bed, as I always did and took his hand.

'Uncle Dunk, I'm home.' He opened his eyes. 'My lassie, my lassie,' he whispered. 'I knew you would come. Oh, how I prayed. God is good.' His eyes filled with tears and I choked back my sobs.

I mustn't cry, I mustn't cry, I kept telling myself, or he will know. I was too young to understand that the old man knew when death was approaching. I rose from my knees and kissed him several times. 'I'm home to stay,' I said, 'as long as you need me. I'll go now and change my good clothes and see you later.'

'Yes,' he whispered, 'you do that and I'll have a wee sleep.' His eyes closed as I left the room.

In the kitchen, Mrs McAndrew arrived and was talking to Aunt Anne. She has come, I thought, out of curiosity. She must have seen me coming along the road. Since leaving I had grown into a tall, slim girl with rather a good figure. So I was told by my staff friends. My best features, seemingly, were my large hazel eyes and thick black hair. So at the sight of me, Mrs McAndrew stared.

'My, my, you've changed,' she said, holding out her hand. I ignored it. 'Hallo, Mrs McAndrew. How is Mary getting on?'

'Fine. She's with Nan in Rothesay. Nan is married now, but you will know that.'

'No, I didn't,' I replied. 'Mrs Fraser wouldn't think of mentioning it, since she had so much else to write about.' The gibe struck home.

Her face reddened. 'Well, I must say they aren't teaching you manners in the South,' she replied tartly. 'I'll go now, Anne, and see you later. You will get a rest tonight. I'll sit with Duncan.'

'Oh no you won't,' I swung round and faced her. I had been picking up my coat and hat when she spoke. 'I am sitting with Uncle Dunk tonight, and every other night, so there will be no need for you, or anyone else, to do so.' I picked up my bag and started up the stairs. A whispered conversation in Gaelic ensued, then Aunt Anne came into my room.

'The bed is not made up. I didn't know you were coming. Was it Jess Fraser who told you?'

'Yes. I received a telegram from her. I am going to see her after I get something to eat,' I said.

'You shouldn't have spoken to Mrs McAndrew like that, Mina,' Aunt Anne said, after a few seconds.

'Why not?' I looked straight at Aunt Anne.

'Well, she's been very good, looking after Duncan for me when I was out about the croft.'

'Oh yes,' I said slowly, 'and when you were at Strathpeffer, remember?'

'Mina, about your holiday,' she said hurriedly, 'you could have gone to Mrs Fraser.'

'Yes, I know that,' I said coldly, 'but would I have been allowed to see Uncle Dunk at Mrs McAndrew's? I am sure, between yourselves, you would make sure that I wasn't allowed to see him on some excuse or other, so what was the use of coming?'

'That's not true, Mina, and you know it.'

'Then why did you not leave Uncle here? You knew I was coming the day you went to Strathpeffer. Were you afraid to leave us alone for a week, in case I would realise how much he had missed me and decide not to return to my job, but stay with him, making the remainder of his life the happier?'

'No, no. That's all wrong. Mina, you are a wicked girl to think that. The worst thing I ever did was to take you into my house.' And with that she turned and left.

When I came downstairs, a meal was set on the white scrubbed table. I went into Uncle's room but he was asleep, and on returning to the kitchen, Aunt was dishing up the midday meal of broth, boiled beef, carrot and turnip. I had forgotten just how good a cook she was. When I first saw the very modern range, the gas cooker and cooking utensils at Inverleith, I often used to wonder how the Glen folk cooked so well on their peat fires, with no electricity and no running water or gas.

I rose after the meal, thanked her and said I would help her to wash up. 'No, no,' she said, 'you go and see Jess Fraser. After all, you don't do this down South. Housemaids don't wash kitchen dishes.' She was talking to me as if I were a stranger, a visitor and without waiting for a reply, she started pouring water into the wash basin from the kettle.

I went in to see Mrs Fraser, thanked her for her letters to me and for sending me the telegram. When we discussed all that happened since I left, I noticed I'd been there two hours. 'Goodness me,' I said and rose, 'I must go, Uncle will be wondering what has happened to me.'

Mrs Fraser put a restraining hand on my arm. 'Mina, what are you going to do about Anne when Duncan goes?'

Jess Fraser was a small, stout woman with the kindly laughing eyes of most stout people. Her heart was as big as her bosom.

'In the first place, Uncle Dunk is not going to die,' I said determinedly, but I knew I was wrong.

She still kept her hand on my arm and looked at me. 'What are you going to do about Anne?' I didn't answer. I hadn't given it a second thought. 'I don't know, Mrs Fraser.'

'Well,' she said, 'it's time you did. Anne is getting on in years and will soon need someone and there's no one but you.'

'She has Meg McKenzie, her cousin. That's someone.'

Mrs Fraser took her hand off my arm. 'Run along, Mina, but think of what I've said.'

When I got home, Aunt Anne met me at the door. 'He is asking for you. I am going for Mrs McAndrew.' I entered Uncle's room and knelt beside his bed. 'Hello, lassie, lift me up a bit.' His voice seemed stronger and I did as he asked. 'Mina,' his hand came over the top of mine as I knelt down again. 'Don't forget Anne when I'm gone and don't blame her for past wrongs. You see, Mina, we all have our faults.'

'Uncle Dunk, you aren't going away and I'll be back in June for my holidays.'

'Promise me, Mina, you will come back in June,' he said earnestly.

'I certainly will,' I said, 'I promise you that. Nothing will keep me away from you, or from the Glen.'

'Promise, whether I'm here or not, that you will come to the Brae House in June.'

I hesitated for a moment or two, then rose, bent over and kissed him on the brow. 'You know Uncle Dunk . . .' I got no further. My right hand was gripped in a tight clasp. 'I want your promise, Mina.'

His eyes were a little glazed. 'If that's what you want Uncle Dunk, I'll come back, I promise.' 'And stay at the Brae House with Anne,' he continued. His voice had become weaker. I nodded. 'I promise.'

His hand slipped back onto the counterpane. I heard voices in the kitchen. Mrs McAndrew was saying something about the minister. Aunt Anne passed me and went into Uncle Dunk's room.

My Uncle never spoke again and died that night at half past ten.

Chapter 12

I thought my heart would break. No one could console me. I didn't give a thought to Aunt Anne, the one who was, perhaps, going to be the most lonely because I was returning to my work immediately after the burial.

Donald and Craig arrived for the funeral. They just stood across the kitchen floor and stared at me, whereas I had eyes for no-one but Craig, dimly hearing the minister's voice, full of sympathy for those left behind. Then suddenly everyone was moving away towards the door and I lost Craig in the crowd. The next time I saw him, both he and Donald were at the top end of Uncle's coffin, which slowly moved away. I didn't look any longer but turned and mounted the stairs to be alone with my grief.

It was Mrs Fraser who entered my room. 'Well,' her voice was cold but under control, 'are you going to lie there and be sorry for yourself? Get down and help Anne and the rest of us to prepare a meal for the men coming back, cold and hungry.'

'I can't—my face.' I spluttered.

'What's wrong with your face? A bit swollen with tears of self-pity, no doubt.'

Self-pity! I turned on Mrs Fraser. 'It's not self-pity, I loved Uncle Dunk the best in all the world.'

'Well, all I can say is you've a queer way of showing it. His wife needs your sympathy and help, so get downstairs.'

The men returned, as Mrs Fraser said, cold and hungry. When fed, they started to return to their homes. They were no longer talking in hushed tones. The whisky they drank had loosened their tongues. One man was saying goodbye to Aunt Anne. 'You have nothing to worry about Anne, that is a fine bonny lassie you have there. She will look after you.'

I turned away my head and my eyes met Craig's. Did he think I was a bonny lassie? I wonder if he ever thinks of me when I'm not here, I asked myself.

The womenfolk started to leave too. Some lifted tablecloths, folded them and put them into their baskets. 'We will wash them ourselves, Anne, if Mina is going away tomorrow. She won't be here to help.' So these table cloths didn't belong to Anne, nor did most of the dishes. The neighbours were lifting the tea sets and dinner sets and putting them into their baskets. I felt ashamed and embarrassed. It never entered my head that Anne had so little and depended on neighbours. I didn't know that Uncle Dunk hadn't worked for over twenty years and that Anne had worked for them both. I didn't know that there was such a thing as rent or rates for homes and grounds, but I was to learn.

I discovered from Craig and Donald that the rent of the croft cost £6 per annum. This had been paid from a small annuity Duncan received, which now stopped on his death. The land was also taxed for the same amount. The neighbours, I understood, would see that Aunt got fed or, on the other hand, the

Parish would help. The Parish was a dirty word to me. Weren't all foster children brought up by their different parishes, and how often was it thrown in their teeth? I was one of them, and I cringed at the word.

'Who are the rent and taxes paid to?' I asked.

'The Seafield Estate,' was the reply. 'Mr McAndrew collects it twice a year from all the crofts round about and sends it to a Solicitor's office in Inverness.

I had thought all the crofts belonged to the people who worked them. I didn't know Balgreig belonged to a larger estate, nor that the people were tenants. The children in Balgreig were not told how their parents or guardians made ends meet, how they had to fight with the soil all year to make a bare living and, at the end of it, pay for the privilege.

Aunt Anne and Meg McKenzie came from the parlour where they had gone after the departure of the neighbours. 'We've had a long talk, Anne and I,' said Mrs McKenzie, 'and it's been decided she'll give up the Brae House. There is a cottage along at Craigend empty, and I've no doubt the rent will be much less than here, so I'm sure your father will pay for it, boys. I'll talk to him when we get home.'

Craigend village was only a mile from Drumoich which meant Aunt would certainly be nearer her cousin. But give up the Brae House . . . Never! Not if I could help it. 'You can't,' I shouted. 'I want the Brae House kept. I don't want to go to Craigend when I come to the Glen, I want to come here. Please, Aunt Anne, don't do this. Don't do this to me.'

Meg McKenzie spoke firmly. 'Thinking of yourself again, Mina, eh? What about Anne? Has she no say?'

'I'll pay for the rent and taxes to Mr McAndrew,' I pleaded desperately.

'You,' Meg laughed, 'and where are you getting the money from?'

'I'll save all my wages and leave my job for one with better pay.'

'I'll pay it,' Craig broke in, his voice as firm as his mother's.

For the first time, Aunt Anne spoke. 'You, Craig?'

'Yes, me.'

I knew Craig had the farm at the Black Isle behind him, now his Uncle's, but one day it would be his.

'Come on, Donald,' Craig said, 'get the horse saddled to the trap, it's time to go.'

'Are you doing this for *her*,' Meg said, pointing a finger at me, 'or Anne?'

'For them both,' Craig replied. He held out his hand to Aunt Anne. 'Don't worry, Anne. Just you stay where you are. I'll see everything is turned over to me. The Brae House is yours and Mina's as long as you both want it.'

If the joy on Aunt Anne's face reflected the joy in my heart, we must have been the happiest people in the world. 'Duncan would have been a very happy man today if he had heard you just now, Craig,' Aunt Anne said.

'He did,' I said quietly.

I felt a touch on my arm. Craig was standing behind me. I faced him. 'Thank you, Craig, for everything.'

He gave a short laugh. 'I like the Brae House too. It brought you to me. I'm going now, Mina. See you in June. I'll write to you. I know your address.' He held out his arms and it seemed the most natural thing in the world for me to slip into them.

'Mina, darling,' he whispered, 'I love you.'

He kissed me full on the lips. 'That is the first kiss I have ever had from a man,' I whispered. 'I kept myself for you, Craig, just as you asked. Except for Uncle Dunk, of course.' We both laughed shyly at each other.

Aunt Anne was saying her cheerio at the door, but Meg scarcely looked at me. I wonder if she has guessed? I thought. Donald knew. As he took my hand he said quietly, 'He hasn't got you yet, Mina.'

I was too happy to dwell on what he said then, but I was to remember it years later.

Chapter 13

Next morning, I left for Inverness with Mr McAndrew in his trap. I told him about the Brae House, how Craig was going to pay the rent and allow Aunt Anne and I stay in it as long as we wanted. We admired the beautiful scenery along the shores of Loch Ness and the lovely ruins of Urquhart Castle, and I wondered, as I had once before with Craig, about this beautiful old ruin, which must have been occupied about a century ago, long before our time. We passed the cemetery and I spoke of the ghosts that were supposed to have been seen there, then crossed the river Ness and on to Inverness.

Mr McAndrew smiled as he helped me down. 'You will likely

marry a boy from the South, Mina, and forget all about the Glen, and us. Cheerio, and see you in June.'

I shook hands, picked up my cases and entered the station. On the train heading for Edinburgh, I thought of Mr McAndrew's words, 'Forget all about the Glen.' That I could never do, as long as my life lasted. There were two reasons why. First, I loved the Glen, rugged, wild, desolate, but beautiful. It was home to me. My other reason was Craig, the man I had loved since I was a child.

We wrote to each other as promised, about my homecoming in June and of our love, a love we promised each other would never die.

At the end of April, Craig's father died of a heart attack. He was grief stricken. I wrote letters of sympathy and of how my heart ached for him at this time. But he was to receive another blow. It seemed Donald was left the farm jointly with young John, his brother. Craig was getting his Uncle's farm in the Black Isle and was expected to take Alex, the other brother, with him when the time came. Meg McKenzie was, of course, to be left at Drumoich for her lifetime and it was also to be Jean's home until her marriage.

As I loved the Brae House, so Craig loved Drumoich—every tree, shrub and acre of ground attached to it, and far more than Donald ever would. I wondered why his father had done this to his eldest son. They seemed to get on well together, and I knew Craig thought the world of his father. The letters I received from Mrs Fraser threw no light on the matter. I asked Aunt Anne about it in one of my letters to her, but when Mrs Fraser replied on her behalf, it was scarcely mentioned, telling only what I already knew.

At this time I gave in my notice to the Castle Folk. The Head Housemaid was in agreement that I should leave. So was the Housekeeper. 'You have been a fifth housemaid long enough,' Kate said, 'and it's time you started climbing up the ladder.'

I went to the Hope Street Registry Office for Servants in Edinburgh and put my name down. A fortnight later, I received a letter to meet the Housekeeper from Turlum Castle in Perthshire, the home of the Earl and Countess of Moncrieff, at a hotel in the west end of Princes Street. I was interviewed and offered the job as third housemaid of five, providing my references were suitable. A week later, the Housekeeper, Mrs Gray, sent for me and told me I was to go to my new post on the 12th June.

I was leaving on 1st June and going home to the Brae House

and Craig. I never was so happy. On the Friday night, 31st May, the staff collected in the staff room, where I was presented with a suitcase, the first I had ever received. It meant that I didn't need to trail the large trunk and bags I had, when I had arrived over three years ago. I took my leave of the staff, knowing I would miss them. After all, I had been in close contact with them all for the past three years, and we often had good times together in the staff hall after our work was finished, and our fall-outs too. With twenty on the staff, all entirely different from each other, there was bound to be friction some-times, although on the whole, we did get on well enough.

Next morning, I left for Edinburgh's Waverley Station. I never once looked back at Inverleith Hall as the chauffeur drove me down the drive.

'Don't you want a last look?' he asked me, 'before you turn the corner?'

'Why?' I said. 'I never wanted to come here in the first place.'

'Well,' he replied, 'why are you going to Turluin Castle? No one is forcing you to do that.'

'I must work and I know no other job,' I said reluctantly. 'It will do until I get married.'

Taking my leave of the chauffeur at the station, I boarded the Inverness train at 11 o'clock. My happiness was complete and all was well with the world.

At five, the train pulled in at Inverness station, and as I walked along the platform, Peter McAndrew waved from the barrier. I handed my ticket to the ticket collector and shook hands with Peter.

'Hallo, Mina,' he said, 'by Jove, you look grand.'

'Hallo, Peter.' I looked around for Craig. 'Are you just yourself?'

'Yes, were you expecting someone else?' Peter picked up my case and without waiting for an answer, started to walk out of the station. I hurried after him, looking round. What happened to Craig? He had said he would meet me and he knew the time of the arrival of the train.

Outside the station, Peter pointed to a motorbike and side-car. 'What do you think of that?' he asked proudly. I smiled as I looked at the vehicle. 'It's lovely,' I said.

'You bet it is, and it's brand new too.'

He threw my case into the side-car. 'You get up behind me.'

We arrived at the Brae House about an hour later. Aunt Anne met me at the door and held out her hand. As I took it in mine, I thought how frail and old she looked, a shadow of the tall, gaunt and tight-lipped woman I had known as a child, whose hand was like leather across my face and legs. I remembered how I had run round Uncle Dunk's chair for protection, pleading with him, 'Don't let her, don't let her.'

I put my case down at the bottom of the stair and entered the kitchen. 'I'll give you a run later, Mina, if you like,' Peter shouted.

'No thanks, Peter, not tonight.'

A look of disappointment crossed his face. 'Oh well, some other night then. Cheerio, be seeing you.'

'Thank you for bringing me home,' I called at his retreating figure.

Uncle Dunk's chair was still there, but I could see it was now used by Aunt. I walked into his room and noticed Aunt was using that too. She was standing behind me and must have read my thoughts. 'I'm not able to climb stairs as well as I used to, and I'm afraid I'll fall when I'm coming down, so I just use this room.'

The resentment that rose inside me cannot be described in words. Uncle Dunk was no longer at the Brae House, and there was nothing left of his presence; it was as if he had never been.

'Where are his things?' I asked in a voice I didn't recognise as my own. I looked at the mantelpiece where his pipe usually lay. It was gone. I looked at the corner of the large fireplace for his crutches. They were gone. I went back into the room and looked behind the door, where his clothes formerly hung. They were gone too, and in their place were clothes belonging to Aunt Anne.

'I gave everything to the McPhee's for dishes and things I needed,' she explained in a quiet voice.

'The McPhees!' I screeched. 'How dare you do that? The tinks with Uncle Dunk's things.' She must have been forced to do it.

'Mina,' her voice was barely a whisper, 'what was the use of them, they were only reminding me of him? I had to get rid of them.'

Oh how cruel youth can be to old age. 'Don't tell me,' I said sarcastically, 'that you cared for him. That's a laugh. Who took him out to sit at the door in the summer? You? No, I did. Who attended to his every need? You? No, I did.'

'I had to work, Mina, remember.'

But I didn't want to remember, I only wanted to hurt this old woman. 'It's you who should have died instead of Uncle Dunk. We wouldn't have thrown your belongings out, he would have

kept them and treasured them. He was far too good for you.'
I turned and walked out of the kitchen, picked up my case and
went upstairs to my room.

It was as neat and tidy as I had left it. I put down my case
and noticed a small hump on the bed. Turning down the
blankets I saw a hot water bottle between the sheets. Aunt Anne
must have come up to do this in case of dampness. For all her
fear of the stairs, she had done this for me. My throat tightened
and tears welled in my eyes. 'Oh God,' I said aloud, 'I'm a
bitch, what came over me?' Was it because I wanted to get my
own back for the way she had treated me as a child, or was it
because of Uncle Dunk? Perhaps the latter but I doubted
that.

It was because Craig hadn't met me at the station as he had
promised that I took my spite out on the old woman downstairs. I turned and descended the stairs.

'Aunt Anne, I didn't mean what I said,' I murmured feebly.
She was sitting on Uncle's chair and as I entered she looked up
with tired eyes from the fire.

'Perhaps some day you will realise what it is like to lose a
loved one.' she said. 'The table is set and your dinner is ready.
Sit in.'

She rose and looked straight at me. Was that pity I saw in her
eyes? But why should she pity me? I'm imagining things, I
thought but, at the same time, I felt a cold shiver run down my
spine. I washed my hands and drew in my chair as Aunt said
grace. She hadn't accepted my attempt at apologising.

Chapter 14

After the pans and dishes had been washed, I tidied up the
kitchen. Aunt Anne lifted her shawl from the chair. 'I'm going
over to Mrs McDonald's for a wee while. She hasn't been well
and I promised I would look in after you had a meal. You can
come if you like. She will be very glad to see you.'

'Wait, Aunt,' I said. I had to ask, I couldn't keep up the
suspense of not knowing about Craig. She sat down and put her
shawl on her knee.

'If it's about Craig, he is at the Black Isle. His Uncle died
yesterday.'

'Why wasn't I told?'

'Well, Donald told Craig he would send you a telegram,' Aunt Anne explained.

'I got no telegram.'

'The funeral is on Monday, so I don't expect you will see him until after that.' Aunt Anne rose and put on her shawl. 'I won't be long, are you coming?' I shook my head.

'No I'll go up the hill a walk,' I replied.

How long I sat looking into the peat fire, I don't know. When at last I rose, I felt something was wrong. But what? I had no idea. What could be wrong? Craig loved me. His Uncle's farm would now be his and we would get married.

As I started walking towards the moor and skirting the Lochan, I just couldn't shake off this feeling I had. I left the Lochan and started to climb. About half a mile further on I stopped and turned. The panorama before me was unbelievable. The Balmacan forest away in the distance rose before my eyes as if in a painting, and beyond the forest were the mountains of the west. Possibly I was looking towards the mountains of Glen Affric, but I didn't know. Below me the crofts and villages of the Glen snuggled cozily in the crisp mountain air. Far to the West was Glen Affric and to the east was Loch Ness and the Cale-donian Canal. Behind me the mountains of Sgur-na-Lapoich could be seen in the distance. I sat on one of the rocks and gazed my fill. I could hear the pee-wees and the curlews and the gulls skimming low over the Lochan searching for fish. There were no deer to be seen. It was summer and they would be well up the mountains behind me, but, I've no doubt they saw me.

After a while, in the quiet solitude of the hills I felt calmer. They always had that effect on me, it seemed like a balm on my soul. I loved the Glen, and my love for Craig seemed to spring from the same source, like an oak tree, it's branches spreading wide towards the sky, while its roots sank deep into the bowels of the earth. I cannot fathom, nor explain it. I only know it was there.

When I arrived back at the Brae House, it was dusk. Aunt Anne looked up. 'I wondered where you had got to,' she said. 'I might have known you would be up the hills. I saw you coming down,' she continued by way of explanation. 'Are you going to church tomorrow?'

I shook my head. 'You know I am not religious.'

'It will do you no harm to go, you know,' she rebuked. 'I'll go and make some cocoa, then I'm going to bed. I'm tired.'

'Donald is coming after church to see you,' Aunt Anne said as she watched me swing the kettle over the fire on its sway. I wasn't much interested in Donald's arrival, but I was interested to know why his father had left him Drumoich, instead of Craig. Aunt Anne didn't go to church either. She said the school meeting at night would do her as she wasn't able enough for the journey to church or the long service.

We heated up the dinner and set the table. I was just taking the beef to the table when Donald came in.

'You must have smelt the soup,' Aunt Anne said as she put down the tureen to shake hands. Donald shook hands with her, then approached me. 'Mina, how are you?' We also shook hands. 'How are you Donald? You look well. Sorry about your Uncle.'

I felt silly and childish. I'm talking a lot of nonsense, I thought, but it was for something to say. I felt his eyes boring into mine, boring into my very heart. I drew my hand away.

'Sit down at the bottom of the table. I've laid a place for you there.'

Aunt Anne was dishing up the soup into our plates. After grace was said, Donald started speaking to Aunt Anne about his Uncle, so there was no need for me to speak, nor even to look at him. I still felt his eyes on me, and I hated it. I could have lifted the soup and thrown it into his grinning face, but what would that achieve? He spoke of his mother and brothers, all except Craig, how his sister Meg now had another boy.

'You really must go to Kirkhill and see Meg, Mina. I promised to take you this time and she will never forgive me if I don't.'

I smiled my thanks, but with no intention of going. I hadn't seen Meg for years and I was sure she would have no interest in me. Donald had probably told her he was bringing me, not the other way round.

'How is Jean?' I asked.

'Fine,' he said, 'she's eleven now and quite clever in school. She is waiting for her exam results and if she has a good mark, she will perhaps get into High School. Drumuir, you know.'

I knew. I remembered I had wanted to go there too and could have made it, but for Aunt Anne and the Aberdeen Authorities backing her up. I hadn't even been allowed to sit the exam.

After dinner (there was no washing up on Sundays) we sat round the peat fire. Somehow I had to get Donald to myself to ask about Craig. 'Would you like to come out for a while,' I asked. Donald rose.

'See you later, Anne. There are eggs and butter from mother on the motorbike. I'll bring them in.' When he joined me, I pointed to the road. I didn't want to share my beloved moor, nor the Lochan with Donald. When we were out of sight of the crofts, he turned off the road towards the planatation.

'You are lovelier every time I see you, Mina,' he said huskily.

'Donald, you forget I'm in love with Craig.'

He laughed. 'Why isn't he here then?'

'His Uncle has died and he is the heir, so he must attend to all the business. You know that yourself.' I said angrily.

'On Sunday, Mina. Don't be silly.' He held out his hand to grip my arm again.

'Keep your hands to yourself, Donald McKenzie. I don't want you to touch me. Let's go back.' I turned and he fell into step beside me.

'Mina, if you marry Craig, he will have nothing.' But I wasn't listening to what he was saying for there in front of us, walking towards me, was Craig. I left Donald's side and ran and ran. My long black hair flew behind me like a cloak. I felt the light summer breeze on my face and my heart was thumping in my breast. I was so happy I thought it would burst. Craig ran towards me too and as we met his arms opened and I threw myself at him. He lifted me high in the air and swung me round and round. As my feet touched the ground, our lips met. 'Mina, my Mina,' he whispered into my hair.

'Oh Craig, Craig.'

We were together. Everything and everyone was forgotten. Our arms entwined each other as we walked towards the Brae House. This was all that mattered, all that would ever matter. We were together. When we arrived back at the Brae House, Aunt was getting ready for the gospel meeting down in the school, which meant Craig couldn't stay. In those days, boyfriends were not allowed to remain alone with their sweethearts without a chaperone.

'I'll be going,' he said, 'and I'll see you on Tuesday. I'm coming back to Drumoich on Monday night after the funeral as there will be things to discuss with my mother.' He held out his hand and took hers. 'I'll see you on Tuesday, Anne.'

She nodded and turned to me. 'You should be coming to the meeting too. Where's Donald?' As Anne mentioned his name I heard his footfall outside the window. We had forgotten all about him. 'I'm sorry we didn't wait for you.' I apologised.

'That's all right, Mina, love does queer things to people,' he said. He looked at us both and laughed. 'Well, I'm off, Anne. Coming, Craig?'

'I'll be right behind you.' Craig's voice when he spoke to

Donald was sharp, his eyes cold and without feeling. Why didn't these two brothers like each other? They always seemed excessively polite when they addressed each other, or downright sarcastic. Perhaps this was how brothers behaved, I thought. I didn't know, having neither brother nor sister.

Craig took me in his arms. 'Until Tuesday sweetheart,' he whispered. I nodded and he was gone.

On Monday, I cleaned the Brae House from top to bottom. Bedrooms were scrubbed and polished, rugs were beaten and laid down, windows were cleaned and kettles, pans and griddle were scraped and black leaded. Water was carried in and the washing done outside beside the boiler fire, then hung up on the wire rope, and in the evening brought in and ironed by heating the iron bolts in the peat fire. When they were red-hot they were taken out and slipped into the iron.

As the evening wore on, Aunt Anne told me to stop. 'You've worked like a hatter,' was her expression. I sat down about nine o'clock that night, admitting I felt a little tired, but I had scarcely noticed, I was so happy. Tomorrow was Tuesday, and Craig was coming.

Tuesday morning was another lovely day. I rose full of the joys of life and made the breakfast of porridge and toast, then cleared the table and washed up. That afternoon, I was bringing in water from the well. 'There's someone coming,' Aunt Anne said, making for the door, 'I hear a horse and trap.'

She was right. As I looked out of the window, Meg McKenzie was drawing up her horse and trap at the gate. She descended and shook hands with Aunt Anne, then she turned to young John who had accompanied her. 'Take the horse out of the trap and turn him loose at the back of the croft.'

This meant she was staying for a few hours at least. There was something strange in her manner as she walked into the kitchen and looked at me. Before she uttered a word, I could see there was something very wrong. 'How are you, Mina? You look well.'

'Are the men back from the Black Isle?' asked Aunt Anne.

'Just Donald. Craig will be tonight sometime,' Meg replied, looking towards me.

'Donald didn't put off much time after the funeral,' said Aunt Anne.

'The funeral was at half past eleven this morning and Donald left immediately after the will was read. You know the rate these motorbikes go at. I hate them.'

'You must have come away just after Donald came home

then,' said Aunt Anne. I could see she was beginning to wonder what had brought her cousin here in such haste.

'Yes, just after that.'

I looked at the clock on the high mantlepiece. It was just half-past four. I sat down opposite Aunt Anne, who was in Uncle Dunk's chair facing the window. Meg was sitting between us with her elbow resting on the table, in the centre of the kitchen. Aunt Anne was silent and so was Meg. I could hear the clock ticking, the quarter-to-five chimes started and then died away. I tried to make my voice casual, but it seemed to come from a great distance.

'Will Craig be coming home tonight, or will he be too late reaching Drumoich?' I asked feebly. 'If he is late, I'm sure he will be very tired, so tell him tomorrow will do.'

'I want you to give Craig up, Mina. He will never give you up, so you must be the one to do so.'

I sat there and stared at Meg McKenzie. Then I looked at Aunt Anne. She was looking at me as I had noticed once before, with pity.

'Mina, that way you won't get hurt,' Meg McKenzie finished.

So that was it! I was a foster child who had been brought up by the parish. Some people were kind to such as me, others weren't. Even when we grew to be adult, we still had to be kept in place and must never wish or hope to marry into the families of the better off. The McKenzies with their 500 acre farm, could certainly come into that category. Northfield, on the Black Isle, the farm that had belonged to Craig's Uncle was 300 acres. I remembered him once telling me that. It was now Craig's, and I wasn't considered good enough for him.

'We love each other, Mrs McKenzie. Don't you understand that. It doesn't matter to Craig who I am or what I am, and I would marry Craig if he were penniless.'

Although my voice was quiet, and low, I felt a rising anger inside that I had never known before. I felt a hatred for these two women who were sitting there so calmly, hands lying idle in their laps, while my world slowly crumbled before me. I hated Aunt Anne for the harsh way she had brought me up, and Meg McKenzie for her initial kindness to me as a child, because now, when I wanted to marry her son and come into her family, she was just not going to have it. My rage and hate must have shown on my face.

It was Meg who spoke at last.

'Mina, you are terribly wrong if you think I don't want you as a daughter. I admit, at first I wasn't too keen, but as time went on, I learned to accept it. You're a good girl and I know you love Craig. That is why I'm here.'

I remained silent. I knew I was going to hear something that was to change my whole life and there was nothing I could do. 'Mina, I want you to listen very carefully.' Meg McKenzie started to speak again. 'I know you wondered why Craig wasn't left Drumoich when his father died, and why it was left to Donald and John instead. Well, I will tell you why, Mina.'

She took a deep breath. 'My husband, as you know, was brought up on Northfield on the Black Isle. There were two brothers, Craig the elder, and my John. I was an only child and when John and I married, my father, Bill McIntosh, asked John to join him at Drumoich, and before he died he gave John the farm. Craig was left with Northfield. When the brothers' father died, Craig discovered the farm was in a bad way financially. John couldn't help, as Drumoich wasn't doing too well either at the time. On lawyer's advice, Craig went into partnership with a Bank Manager called Robert Leitch. Robert's interest in the farm was nil, but his money put Craig on his feet. Craig and John were very close, and they saw each other often.

'When my son was born, Craig asked if he could be called after him, which we did, and gladly. At every opportunity, he took Craig, his nephew, to Northfield and treated him like a son, with the result that Craig came to love Northfield and, as he grew up, he was never away from his Uncle. The final result was he was made his Uncle's heir. When my husband made his will, it was decided, Donald and John should share Drumoich and Craig was to have Northfield with Alex, until the younger boys got married, then Donald and Craig were to help them to buy a place of their own. Uncle Craig was notified of this and was agreeable. But he didn't reckon with Robert Leitch.

'Robert had an only child, a daughter. When he died, he made a will making his daughter Elizabeth, a full partner with Uncle Craig or his heirs. If the young Craig married Elizabeth Leitch, the whole farm was to be transferred to him. If not, then her share was to be returned.

'That share is now quite considerable. It means that more than half of the land would have to be sold, also a great deal of the livestock. I have no doubt Craig's Uncle meant to buy Elizabeth out before he died. but he never had the money. He certainly wasn't a good husbandman, not like his brother John. We knew nothing about all this and were always under the impression the money had been paid back and the farm was Craig's in its entirety. The will was read out this morning and

Donald brought me the news. That's what I'm doing here, Mina.'

'For you, Craig would sell half of the farm and livestock which would reduce the farm to little more than a croft. Can you see Craig farming a place the size of the Brae House croft and working for another farmer to make ends meet. It would take twenty years to build Northfield to what it is now. Is that what you want, Mina? Craig will be paying a very high price for you if that is to be the way of it.'

I remained silent. 'You are far too young, anyway, to think of getting married. You should be out enjoying life, not thinking of marriage, at your age.'

I stood up without speaking, grabbed a light coat from the hook on the wall of the lobby and stepped outside. The evening sunlight struck me on the face as I raised my head to say 'goodbye' to John who was climbing onto the trap. 'Cheerio,' he called, 'see you soon.'

I turned at the end of the cottage, making my way up towards the moor. I cannot explain how I felt. I just wanted to be alone and think. I reached the moor, skirted the Lochan and started to climb the hill, just going up and up, passing crags and through heather. My stockings were ripped but I didn't care. At last, tired and exhausted, I came to a small plateau covered in green grass. The hill sheep scattered at my approach and I fell face downward. How long I remained there, I don't know, but after a while I sat up and raised my eyes.

The sun was setting away to the west. I would have to go back down.

At first I thought I heard a sheep or goat coming towards me, but looking back, I saw old Bell McPhee, with her pack on her back. The McPhee tinks were well known in the Glen. There was never a door shut in their faces and always a bed in the hayloft on cold frosty nights. In the summer, we didn't see so much of them. They were away, "on the road" as they called it. Their tents were usually down on the shores of Loch Meikle or over at Lochlitter. To see Bell, an old tink here and alone, was a surprise, especially so high up Tomnaloich.

'Goodness me, lassie, what are you doing up here, eh?' She was as surprised to see me as I was to see her. 'You will be Anne Gordon's lass?' she asked.

I nodded. She untied her pack and dropped it on the ground, then sitting beside me she drew out her clay pipe and started to smoke. For several minutes she remained silent and when she spoke again it was a mixture of Gaelic and English, very much like the older people of the Glen. 'How old are you now, then?'

'I'll be eighteen on the 11th of this month,' I said.

'Ahh, they don't often come back, the orphans I mean. Why have you?'

I looked at this old woman beside me. I looked into her black piercing eyes. Her hair, once like black ebony, was streaked with grey, her clothes old and torn in places. Her boots were worn and tied with string. For stockings she had men's socks, but yet, there was a dignity about her. A calmness. Before I realised, I was pouring out my story, starting with my childhood just as I've related it here. When I had finished, it was getting dark.

'Come,' she rose slowly. 'Let us go down. Perhaps McAndrew or some of them will give me a straw bed for the night.' I rose and turned to go as Bell picked up her pack and began to tie it on her back. 'Lassie, look at me,' she said.

I turned.

'Get ye away down to the South, where your future lies. There you will meet your man and marry. Your sons will grow to manhood and you will have cause to be proud of them. Proud, because you will bring them up in the fear of God and in the knowledge that they will go from strength to strength.'

I stared hard at her. I could hardly see her face now, it was so dark.

'And Craig?' I asked.

She started to climb down and I followed. There was silence until we reached the Lochan side and started to cross the moor, towards the Brae House.

'Bell,' I asked, 'what about Craig?'

'I see great character in your face, lassie. You will have the strength to say what you have to. Peace will come with time. You'll see.'

We reached the gate of the Brae House and with that, Bell waved and turned away towards McAndrew's farm. I never saw her again.

Entering the cottage, Aunt Anne looked up anxiously. 'Where have you been?' I looked up at the clock. It was eleven o'clock. 'Make yourself something and get to bed. You were very rude, walking out like that, and Meg not even away,' Aunt Anne rebuked.

I didn't answer. What was the use? I could never tell Aunt my feelings about anything.

'What are you going to do about Craig and yourself?'

'I don't know,' I answered.

'If you marry him next year, you will have to live here. There will be nowhere else. Craig will never live at Northfield with it split up to pay a debt. He will likely put Alex in to work the place.'

Oh God, I thought, why didn't people sort out their money and property before they died and save the living heartache and misery. 'I'm going to bed,' she said, 'we will talk in the morning.' The room door shut behind her.

I sat on Uncle Dunk's chair. If only he had been here! I climbed the stairs, entered my room and undressed and was about to climb into bed when I found myself on my knees. I hadn't prayed since I had last knelt at Uncle Dunk's knee, and for the first time in my life I wanted to. My prayer was simple. 'Oh God help me, please help me.'

Chapter 15

Next morning, I was up at dawn. I came downstairs and started breakfast. When it was ready Aunt Anne appeared.

'You are early. What time is it?' she yawned.

'Too early for you getting up, Aunt. Go back to bed and I'll bring your porridge through to you.'

She shook her head. 'I'm up now.'

After grace was said, Aunt Anne looked at me. 'Did you sleep at all?' I shook my head. 'The day will be a long one,' she complained.

It is funny that I remember every small piece of light conversation that was spoken that day. Nothing said or done has escaped me, even after all these years. It is as clear now as it was then.

At eleven o'clock, the sound of a motorbike caught my ears and my heart started to thud. I didn't need to look out of the window for I knew who it was. The bike stopped at the gate and was silenced. Aunt Anne was at the door.

'Hallo, Craig,' I heard her say, 'nice day again.'

'Hallo, Anne,' he answered, 'yes, it's nice. Mina in?'

I heard his feet on the gravel path. 'Yes, she is.'

A moment later he was standing on the threshold of the kitchen door. He was smiling as he stepped inside, and his arms went out to embrace me. It seemed the most natural thing in the world to have his arms around me. He kissed my cheeks, eyes and throat, his hands pushed back my hair and looking into my eyes he said quietly, 'Mina, I will never forget the way you look at this moment. You are beautiful.'

I pushed him gently away. 'Craig, we must talk.'

'Nothing to talk about, Mina.' His voice was firm. 'I'm selling Northfield. The Leitchs' will be paid off and so will the debts, then we can get married and live here. I'm still paying the rent of the Brae House.

'Debts, Craig?' I asked curiously. 'What debts?'

'Oh, Uncle was a very bad manager. He incurred several debts, so I must sell.'

'If the Leitchs leave their share in and part of the livestock, would you then carry on?'

'Oh yes, certainly.' He was about to say something else, instead he looked at me hard. 'What do you mean, Mina, if the Leitchs didn't take out their share. There is no question about whether or not they want their share. They are getting it and that's all about it.'

'And Alex, what about him? Will he come to the Brae House too?'

'Mina,' Craig looked puzzled. 'What's this all about?'

'Your mother was here yesterday and told me about the Will,' I said.

'I know, that's why I didn't arrive last night to see you. There was a family discussion. Mina, I don't care about anything or anybody but you.' He turned away impatiently towards the window. 'Alex can work, the same as me.' His voice trailed away.

I knew Craig well. Too well not to know the turmoil that was going on inside him. He loved Alex and often I'd heard him say, 'When we farm Northfield, lad, we will make a great job of it and when you are ready to marry, there will be enough to buy Laverock.'

I understood this was a small farm close to Northfield, run by two elderly brothers. I knew this to be a dream they both shared and it wouldn't crash to the ground because of me.

I went over to him and, turning, he caught me to him. In his arms, I felt I had the strength to say what I had to. 'Craig, what is Elizabeth Leitch like?'

He raised my chin with his finger. 'Nothing like you, Mina. She is fair, where you are dark. Your eyes are hazel, hers are blue. You are taller than her. You are beautiful, she is not.'

I slipped out of his arms and turned towards the peat fire, which was nearly out, so I lifted a clod from the scuttle and placed it on. 'Let's get out of here Mina and go for a walk. I hear Anne coming in.'

I nodded and Craig took my hand. We met Aunt Anne at the door. 'We are going for a walk,' I said.

Aunt Anne looked at us inquiringly. 'Don't be long then. Dinner will be ready at one.' I nodded. We walked in silence, past Mrs Fraser's cottage and on towards the Plantation. I felt empty inside for I knew as sure as day follows night that this was to be our last meeting together. We sat down under the shade of the pine trees. Craig was kissing me tenderly on the cheek.

'Mina,' he whispered. 'Don't break my heart.' So he knew too.

'You said back at the house you didn't care for anything or anybody. That's not true, Craig. You love Northfield and you love your brother.' I tried to reason with him. 'To give them up would break your heart and turn you into a sour and embittered old man.'

I did not know where I was getting the words and the strength to talk like this, giving up everything I loved. Craig, The Brae House and the Glen. When the parting came it would have to be final. To return might mean that Craig would hear and come to see me. That, I knew, would mean a clandestine affair and that was not for Craig or me. When I returned to the South, it would be forever.

'I am giving you up, Craig,' I said finally.

'Mina!' He held me as if in a vice. 'Don't, Mina. Don't do it. Nothing matters except our love. Nothing.' His voice was thick with emotion.

'It does, Craig. The world outisde matters. People, like Alex for instance. He matters.

'Damn Alex. Damn Uncle Craig for making this happen. And damn Elizabeth Leitch,' he said vehemently.

'Is she in love with you, Craig?'

He was silent for a moment or two. He didn't have to answer me. I knew. His hesitation was enough. 'I don't love her, Mina, so let's leave it at that.' He let go my arms. I rose. 'We'd better get back.'

Craig jumped up. 'Tell you what, Mina. Let me take you to the Black Isle.' I nodded as cheerfully as I could. 'That will be nice.'

'Right, that's settled. Now let's go back to the Brae House and have something to eat. I'm starving. And let's have no more speeches about giving me up. I'm not letting you go, Mina, and that's that.'

I didn't answer and we returned, hand in hand, to the cottage.

At three o'clock, Craig said he had to go. 'I'll pick you up at eleven tomorrow, Mina.'

I nodded. 'You will love Northfield,' he said happily. 'We will manage somehow. We will live at the Brae House for a while after we are married and Alex and I will work hard, and before we know it, we will look back at Northfield and the present will be just like a bad dream.'

Who was he wanting to reassure, himself or me?' If I had had any doubts before, I had none now. Craig would never get over the loss of Northfield, not even one single stone or blade of grass.

'Goodbye Craig,' I held out my hand and he drew me to him. I put my head on his shoulder. 'See you in the morning.'

'Mina, my Mina, and you thought you could give me up.' He laughed, turned towards Anne and said, 'Cheerio,' then climbing on his motorbike, he started the engine and with a wave of his hand he was gone.

I stood staring after him. With him went everything in the world I had ever wanted. Goodbye, Craig, I will never forget you. I turned, walked indoors, climbed the stairs and started to pack. At eleven o'clock tomorrow morning, when Craig was arriving at the Brae House to pick me up, I would be boarding the Perth train at Inverness.

Chapter 16

Aunt Anne looked at me questioningly as I helped her to prepare our dinner. 'Why did he run away like that, without something to eat?'

'It won't take him long to reach Drumoich,' I replied, 'and it is dinner time there too.' And after we had sat down at the table, she asked me, 'What is going to happen then?'

'I will be going to my new job tomorrow. Craig doesn't know. He thinks he is coming to take me to the Black Isle.'

'You know what you are doing, I suppose?'

'What else can I do, Aunt Anne?' I rose from the table pushing away my dinner. 'Have you a better suggestion?'

'I wish you wouldn't go down South again. I have no one to look after me. You could easily get a job nearer home you know. The Bruces from Balnaglaigh are looking for a housemaid, Mrs McAndrew was telling me. You could get home at nights. It's only about three miles away and with a bike you wouldn't be long.'

'You have surely changed your tune,' I said. 'Three years ago you couldn't get me far enough away. If only you had said that when I left school I would have thanked you from the bottom of my heart.' I turned away and made for the door. 'I'm going upstairs to pack.'

'Mina,' her voice rose as if to rebuke me, and she crossed the kitchen floor to where I was standing. 'Mina . . .' she got no further. Her hand went to her throat and a moment later she crashed to the floor. Oh God, she's dead, I thought. I was terrified.

I ran for a cup of water and tried to revive her, but it was hopeless. I thought that if I could raise her head it would help her breathe again, and I pulled my cardigan off to put under her head, then ran for help to the McAndrews' house as it was nearest. I burst in without ceremony.

'It's Aunt Anne, she is lying on the floor,' I gasped.

Mrs McAndrew was washing the dinner dishes. She looked up surprised as I burst in, but quickly dropped her dish-towel. 'Come, Andrew,' she said to her husband, quietly but quickly. 'Run, Peter, and get your motorbike and go to Drumm for Dr McDonald.'

Mr McAndrew, with the help of his wife and myself managed to get Aunt Anne to bed. It took the doctor only an hour to arrive which was good going. By the time he came in the small kitchen was full. Mrs Fraser, Mrs McDonald and Mrs McMillan were in along with their menfolk. Mrs McAndrew came through from the small bedroom and spoke in the Gaelic to Mrs McDonald. 'She is still alive.'

I was completely ignored, and, now that the doctor had arrived, I took the chance to slip upstairs. I looked at my case lying under the table by my bed. There was not much point in starting to pack with Aunt Anne lying downstairs. It would take a very hard hearted person to do that, and I wasn't that type, no matter what I thought of Aunt Anne as a person. She was lying downstairs ill, and I knew it was my duty to look after her.

The men were leaving and as I got back down to the kitchen the doctor looked up. 'I believe you are on holiday,' he said. I nodded. 'When are you due to return south.'

'I go back on the 14th June to a new post.'

He snapped his gladstone bag closed. "Just over a week,' he mused, then nodded his head. 'I'll be back tomorrow. See you then.' I walked to the door with him and watched him ascending his trap, then he touched his horse with the whip and was gone. Mrs Fraser came to the door. 'I'm going now, Mina, so see you later.' Her hand touched my arm. 'All we can do now is pray.'

Mrs McDonald and Mrs McMillan followed her out, muttering sympathetic words as they passed, but I wasn't listening. Mrs McAndrew was still in the kitchen and I didn't want her there. She was bending over the fire as I came in. 'We mustn't let the fire go out, Mina. Will you get in some peat? I don't see any in the scuttle and I want to make some gruel for Anne.'

'Mrs McAndrew, I can manage without help. I know you mean well, but there's no need for you to stay.' She straightened up her back and looked at me hard. 'Now look here my girl, it's not Anne you are talking to, but me, so just watch what you are saying. Now run along and get that peat.'

I kept my hand on the brass knob of the kitchen door. 'I wish you to go, Mrs McAndrew.' My voice was quiet and controlled. 'Thank you for coming when I went for your help, but I'll manage now.'

She came over to the door and stood facing me. For a moment I thought she was going to strike me. If she was, she thought better of it. 'What are the paupers coming to,' she said, and swept past me. I closed the door behind her and went over to sink into Uncle Dunk's chair.

She's not going to order me about, Uncle Dunk, I said to myself. I'll look after Aunt Anne for you, don't you worry. I rose and went into the room. Aunt Anne was lying with her eyes closed as if sleeping, her face grey and drawn. How could anyone be so still and remain alive? The bedclothes didn't seem to move. The whole room was holding its breath. I turned and walked back into the kitchen.

How long I sat there I don't know, but I suddenly felt helpless and alone. I wasn't accustomed to illness, as I worked mostly with young people and was always in their company. The older members of the staff at my old job always seemed to be in the best of health and this was something I couldn't understand.

I must get out, I thought, and was making for the door when I heard the gate swing open. I looked out of the window and saw Mrs Fraser coming up the path to he door. I ran to meet her.

'Oh Mrs Fraser, I'm afraid,' I gasped.

'Where is Mrs McAndrew?' she asked, looking round.

I told her what had happened, and without speaking she went into the room to look at Anne.

A few minutes later she entered the kitchen. 'The injection from the doctor will keep her asleep for a while,' she said. 'Will you go for peat for me? The fire is nearly out.' I returned the smile and went. When the fire was going again, I asked what was the matter with Aunt Anne.

'She has taken a stroke and I think she will be paralysed down the left side,' she answered. 'Her speech might be affected too, but we don't know yet. If she lives, I'm afraid you will have a job on your hands and you won't get help from Mrs McAndrew. You saw to that. When she tells Mrs McDonald and Mrs McMillan, there will be no help from that quarter either. Mrs McAndrew's word is law, you know. Oh they will ask for Anne, but that will be all, as long as you are here.'

'What about you, Mrs Fraser?' I asked sheepishly. 'Will you go by what she says too?'

'No lassie, Kate McAndrew and I crossed swords years ago. We understand each other perfectly. She won't try to influence me in any way, which if I may say so, is a good thing for you, lady.'

I made a cup of tea and as we ate one of Aunt Anne's home-baked scones, we talked, or at least I did, telling Mrs Fraser about Craig and myself, and that I had intended to be gone by the time he came tomorrow. She heard me in silence, then when she had finished her tea, laying the cup carefully in its saucer, she said slowly, 'Do you care for him that much, Mina?'

I nodded. She took a hard look at me, rose from the chair and went to Aunt Anne's room, returning in a few moments. 'You'd better get some sleep and I will sit here for a while, and Mina, remember, there are men who would give their right arm for a love like yours.'

When I awoke about nine o'clock that night and came down-stairs, Mrs Fraser had a meal ready.

'How is she?' I asked.

'She's conscious, I'm glad to say, and not as bad as we thought Her speech is a little slurred, but it isn't too bad. I must go home now, Mina. Will you be all right?' She looked at me anxiously. 'I'll send Andrew along to sit with you for a while. It will break the monotony.'

I went into Aunt Anne's room. She was lying propped up as Mrs Fraser had left her. 'How are you Aunt Anne?' I asked kindly.

'I am able to speak, thank God,' she whispered.

'You gave me a right fright falling like that. Now, what would you like.'

She shook her head. 'Mrs Fraser gave me some gruel. I'm all right. Mina, are you still leaving tomorrow?'

I shook my head. 'What do you take me for? I'm going to look after you as long as I'm needed.'

'But what about your job?' she asked.

She had closed her eyes before I could reply, and I saw that she was dozing, so I rose from the bedside chair and returned to the kitchen. I was trying to busy myself tidying up when Andrew Fraser came in. I was delighted to see him. It was, after all, several years since we had last met. We talked of many things, of all that had happened to us since we last saw each other. Andrew had become a brick-layer in Inverness, staying with his mother's sister until he was married last year. He was now the proud father of a baby boy. It was while he was showing me a photo of his family, that I heard Aunt Anne. She was trying to sit up. 'You mustn't exert yourself, Aunt Anne,' I said, pushing her gently back on to the pillows.

'Mina,' she gasped, 'I can't feel my arms or legs.' At least she can speak, I thought, thank goodness for that. 'It will be all right, Aunt Anne,' I told her. 'You fell on the kitchen floor and the doctor has been. He is returning tomorrow. Andrew Fraser is in the kitchen,' I went on, 'I'll ask him to send his mother.'

I escorted Andrew to the door and had said goodnight when I heard Aunt Anne again. I went back into the room.

She was lying flat on her back, trying to say something I couldn't catch. 'Wait till I get the lamp lit,' I said, 'it's getting dark.' I laid the lamp down on the chest of drawers, near her bed. 'There, that's better,' trying to sound cheerful. I stayed on the chair at the foot of the bed, but somehow I couldn't kneel down on the floor and hold her hands, as I had with Uncle Dunk. I just kept sitting there, staring at her. What could I say to comfort her? Nothing, because there was nothing inside me for this poor sick woman.

Why couldn't I love her, just a little? Why couldn't I go over and brush the grey strands of hair off her brow, and perhaps stroke her head? God help me, I couldn't. I wanted to, desperately, but I just sat there, staring.

Her voice was a little slurred, but I could just make it out. 'What are you going to do about tomorrow?' she asked.

'Nothing, I am staying to look after you,' I answered.

I sat in silence again, wondering if I should offer her something to eat or drink, when the door opened. I jumped up, glad to be on the move. As I entered the kitchen, Mrs Fraser met me.

'Thank goodness you're here,' I said relieved. 'I feel useless.'

Mrs Fraser, without speaking, entered the sick room while I waited outside. When she eventually came into the kitchen, I was sitting in Uncle's Dunk's chair. She looked at me for a long time and when she spoke her voice was firm.

'Mina, I want you to go to Anne and make your peace with her.'

'What do you mean?' I asked.

'Just what I said, make your peace with her now. She is the only mother you ever knew.'

'I can't get through to her, Mrs Fraser,' I said. 'You know that. Even as a child I couldn't.'

'You are not a child now, Mina. Anne did what she thought was right. Perhaps it was rough and at times cruel, but that was her way. It hasn't done you any harm, as far as I can see,' she added. 'You are a very proud and arrogant girl. Perhaps Anne saw that in you as a girl and tried to curb it. I don't know.'

'I can't, Mrs Fraser. I can't,' I said finally.

'Mina, Anne is dying. Does that mean nothing to you? Go to her, lass, and I'll have something for us to eat when you come back.'

I entered the sick room where Aunt Anne was lying very still. Her eyes were open and as I stood near the bed, they were fixed on my face.

'Do you want something, Aunt Anne?' I said feebly.

She shook her head slowly. When she spoke, her voice was weak, and I had to lean over her to hear what she had to say. 'The Brae House and Craig.'

The two names I loved most in the world was the last thing I expected Aunt Anne to say. I didn't want her mentioning them. I didn't want to talk about that. Anything but that.

'Don't worry about a thing, Aunt Anne. I'm staying at the Brae House and looking after you,' I repeated. 'I promised Uncle Dunk you know, to see you were all right. Are you sure you don't want anything?'

Her eyes never left my face. I felt she was seeing right through me, deep into my very soul and could read every thought, and then without realising what I was doing, I was suddenly on my knees at her bed. I drew one of her hands from under the blankets. It was cold. I pressed it to my cheek. 'Aunt Anne, don't die, please don't die.' My voice was cracked with emotion. 'If you do, I have no one. I can't marry Craig. If I do, he will have to give up Northfield. The farm is heavily in debt and to give the Leitchs back their share, he will have to sell. And I can't do that to him, Aunt Anne. Northfield has been to him what the Brae House is to me.'

I put her cold hand back between the sheets, and as I looked up at her face I was amazed. Her eyes shone like stars. When she spoke her voice seemed to gain strength.

'I have made a good job of you, after all. Your Uncle Dunk would have been proud of us both.' Her voice started to weaken. 'You will meet someone who will make you happy.' With that her voice trailed into silence, while I sat with her.

Aunt Anne died that night.

I had taken Mrs Fraser's advice and made my peace with her, at least I hope she had thought so. We were closer in those last ten minutes than we had ever been during the years I lived with her at the Brae House.

Chapter 17

What happened after Aunt Anne died is, looking back on it now, a blur in my memory. I remember Mrs McDonald telling me to go home with her to get some sleep and I gratefully accepted.

All Aunt Anne's lying-out clothes were upstairs in the big kist in the spare room along from mine, and I was kept busy looking out clean sheets and the other things we needed. The room where she lay had to be scrubbed, which I did, as there would be no time in the morning. At her house Mrs McDonald showed me into her spare room, where I instantly fell asleep.

In the morning, I thanked Mrs McDonald and went back to the Brae House, which was now full of visitors. Some I knew, others I didn't, but I didn't care who they were. Craig was standing talking to someone at the kitchen window and my heart gave a great leap. He was coming towards me, his hand outstretched. One didn't throw oneself into a loved one's arms in a house of mourning. But that didn't bother me because his eyes told me all I wanted to know. 'I'm sorry about Anne,' he said, holding my hand.

From somewhere in the kitchen, I heard his mother's voice. 'Anne is better away. If she had lived, she would never have got up again.' She too came and shook hands.

I was being introduced to strangers I had never seen, yet their names were Gordon and McKenzie. They looked prosperous enough to me, so why hadn't I ever seen them visiting the Brae House and offering to help Uncle Dunk and Aunt Anne, who God knows, needed it. I was to remember and think about this again, but this was neither the time nor place for reflection.

I didn't get Craig to myself that day. He was away most of the time with someone called James Gordon, making all the funeral arrangements. I wanted desperately to get out of the house and make for the hills and moors, but I had to stay and make small talk. When Craig did come back and was ready to take his mother home, he first drew me aside.

'I won't see you until the funeral on Saturday, Mina, but the Brae House, as you know, is in Anne's name, so I'm going to the Factor's Office tomorrow to change it to mine. That will be quite in order as I've been paying the rent, so there is no problem there. I will also have to go to Inverness to see my Uncle's lawyer about Northfield,' he added.

'Craig,' I stopped him. 'Don't do anything about Northfield until after the funeral. Nor the Brae House. Promise me.'

He smiled down at me, his fine eyes full of love. 'Mina,' he said, surprised, 'why ever not?'

What excuse could I give him? I had one moment's blind panic. He must never know what I intended to do after the funeral. The first parting was bad enough, but this was going to be a thousand times worse. 'Well,' I said, gathering my words carefully, 'I want to go with you when you get the Brae House. After all, it's going to be our home.' I turned my head away. I couldn't look at him lest he saw the pain in my eyes. 'And you were going to take me to the Black Isle, remember?'

'Of course. All right, we will leave it over till next week.'

Quickly, I started to speak to someone behind me. Anything to hide the ache in my heart. Next week was aeons away, but I dared not think about it just now.

Saturday turned out a beautiful day. I had refused to give myself time to think since Aunt Anne died. I brought dishes from Mrs Fraser's, tablecloths from Mrs McAndrew. I could have sent someone else for the tablecloths, but I had a job to do at Mrs McAndrew's, and that was to apologise for my rudeness to her.

She accepted it in a half-hearted way. 'You are going to get yourself into a lot of trouble with that tongue of yours,' she said, handing me over her best linen.

After the service, Aunt Anne left the Brae House for the last time. She's lucky, I thought. Knowing I can never return will be something I have to live with for the rest of my life. But I quickly brushed the tears from my eyes. The mourners would think I was crying for Aunt Anne, and I wasn't. I was being sorry for myself.

When the men returned, everything was ready. During the meal, I looked around me at the strangers—the Gordons and McKenzies I had met—and an anger rose in me. Who were the two men with the name of Gordon? Where did they live and what did they do? It was during a lull in the conversation that I turned to the elderly man across the table from me.

'Are you a relation of my Uncle Duncan's?' I asked.

There was dead silence. Everyone looked at me as if I had committed some hideous crime.

'Mina!' Mrs McKenzie's voice was disapproving.

'That's all right, Meg,' said the man, 'Yes, my girl, I'm his brother.' He then turned away to speak to Mr McAndrew, as if I didn't exist.

'And you?' I asked the man sitting beside him, who was also a Gordon. 'Are you his brother too?' Another deathly silence.

'Yes,' came back the answer like the crack of a whip. I rose from my chair.

'What do you do and where do you stay?' I asked.

The elder of the two, at least I took him to be as he looked older, said looking up at me, 'Impertinence!'

Someone told me sit down. I couldn't. This anger inside me grew and grew.

It was Craig's voice speaking. 'James and Bob Gordon are farmers at Corriemony.'

Only ten miles away, I thought, and poor Uncle Dunk sat here, chained to a chair for over twenty years, depending on the charity of good neighbours. Aunt Anne's back was bent. An old woman before her time.

The anger inside me burst. 'How dare you come here, with your crocodile tears and flowers? You didn't help them in life, so why bother in death?'

I almost shrieked at them. 'Get back to where you belong, you hypocrites. And as for you, whoever you are—a McKenzie, so you must be related to Aunt Anne—that goes for you too.'

I pushed back my chair. The silence was so acute that the scraping of the chair on the slab floor seemed like a scream. Everyone in the room seemed to wonder what to do next. It was Craig who rose and came to stand beside me. 'She is right, you know,' he said quietly, and he took my hand.

'Let's go, Mina. Let's get out of here.' We were well over the moor before I spoke.

'They could have helped, Craig, couldn't they?'

'Yes, they could have.'

'Then why didn't they?'

'I'm not sure.' A frown crossed his face. 'My mother could tell you. Some feud or other I think. Duncan's family disowned him when he married Anne. He was a farmer's son and she was a servant.'

We walked on in silence.

'This Mr McKenzie?' I asked.

'He is a cousin of Anne's and also a cousin through marriage to mother. They haven't much, just a small croft near Glen Affric.'

'Craig, I'm sorry about that outburst, but I couldn't help it. When I saw the Gordons so prosperous looking . . .' My voice broke. I was sobbing. Craig drew me to him.

'Let's sit beside the Lochan here.' He drew me down beside him and kissed me hungrily. 'Mina, we will be married as soon as possible, say three months. That will give me time to clear everything up and move into the Brae House.'

I drew away from him, dried my eyes and rose to my feet. 'Craig, we will have to go back, the visitors will be leaving. When everyone has gone, then we will talk.'

He stood up reluctantly. 'All right,' he said, kissing me on the nose. My heart was like lead.

When we got back to the Brae House, the Gordons had gone, so also had the menfolk from round about. The women were packing the dishes and tablecloths were being folded. Just a repeat of Uncle Dunk's funeral. No one spoke to me, so I slipped up to my room. I had committed the cardinal sin of voicing my opinion of the Glen folk in public. A pauper, a girl brought up on the Parish, daring to raise her voice against the system. These people were Highland, proud and arrogant, and brooked no interference from outside their ranks. But they had hearts of gold in their way. I knew that too.

But they were also unforgiving, as must have been the case with Uncle Dunk when he strayed from the fold and married Aunt Anne. That was why Aunt had become so bitter in the midst of plenty. Uncle Dunk had nothing because of his marriage to her. It might have been different if he had kept his health. Who knows? So that was why the look of joy had came into Aunt Anne's face when I told her I wasn't marrying Craig and why. She hadn't wanted us to suffer as she and Duncan had, and I didn't even belong to the Glen.

Someone was calling my name downstairs. I rose and hurried down. Mrs Fraser was just leaving. 'I'll see you later, lassie,' she said.

When I entered the kitchen, the McKenzies were all there

and Donald was speaking. 'You can't give it up Craig, and you know it.'

'What can't he not give up, Donald?' I asked quietly.

He came over to me. 'You know what we are talking about, Mina. Northfield.'

'Oh yes, Northfield,' I replied. 'Was it to save Craig from marrying me, Donald, that you proposed?'

A gasp went round the kitchen. Craig's eyes blazed as he approached his brother. 'You proposed to Mina?'

'It's all right, Craig.' I stood between them. 'He didn't mean it. Donald doesn't even like me.' I turned away and stood at the window looking out. I had grown up these last few days, from a girl to a woman, for all my young years. Would I really have gone before Aunt Anne took ill? My intentions were good. I was going to pack and leave on the first bus and be a long way off before Craig arrived at the Brae House to take me to the Black Isle.

That was a few days ago, and I wondered now if I could have really gone through with it. If I had stayed, what then? Happiness with the man I had loved since I was a child, or would it be remorse and, later, bitterness on both sides, while we tried to scrape a living from the Brae House with Craig out on hire to farmers to make ends meet? I had never known anything else but poverty, but not so Craig. The farm at Drumoich was large, as was Northfield, and there was money to be made there. With careful handling, I knew Craig had it in him to make North-field work. And the Brae House? No, not for Craig. I loved him too much.

I came away from the window. The two men had turned from each other and sat down. Their mother had risen. In times of crisis, tea was the order of the day, even in the remote Glen.

'I'll just put on the kettle, Mina, and you set the table,' Meg McKenzie said. 'We don't need much to eat, but a cup of tea will be just fine.'

Alex was winding up his watch and saying something to John about getting back to Drumoich. 'I'm going out for a few minutes,' said John rising, 'I'll water the horse and saddle him to the trap if we're leaving after tea.'

'I'll help,' Alex offered, standing up.

As they passed Craig, they both looked at him with a question in their eyes. Were they trying to tell him not to be a fool? I didn't and will never know. So here we were. The three people who had played such a big part in my life, together for the last time. They didn't know that, but I did.

Mrs McKenzie started to make the tea and I went to the dresser, bringing out cups and saucers, sugar and cream. The two boys returned and we each picked up a cup as Mrs McKenzie poured. The talk was general.

I was washing the dishes to put them away, when John said, 'Ready, mother?' She rose and stood beside me.

'Are you going to stay with one of the neighbours for the rest of your holiday, Mina? You can come to Drumoich if you wish, you know that.'

I held out my hand. 'Goodbye, Mrs McKenzie, and thank you. But no, I'm going away on Monday morning.'

Craig was at my side in a flash.

'Mina, you are not.' He gripped my arm and swung me round to face him. Slowly, I released my arm, shook hands with his mother, Alex and John, and then walked to the door to see them off. As Alex passed me, I touched his arm.

'Alex, you can go to Northfield any time, and take Craig with you.' The smile on Alex's face was a joyful sight.

'Gosh, Mina, you are the tops,' he beamed.

'Look after him, Alex, and farm Northfield as it should be farmed.'

'I will, Mina, don't worry and . . . thanks. I'm sorry you're not going to be my sister-in-law. I mean that.'

I went back to the kitchen. Donald was standing at the window smiling. 'Alex seems very pleased with himself, I wonder why?' he said, still smiling as he turned.

'You know why, Donald,' I said. I wanted to wipe that smile off his face, but instead I held out my hand. 'Goodbye, Donald. Your motorbike is at the door, so it won't take you long. You will be home before your mother if you go now.'

'I'll have to wait for Craig,' he retorted. 'He hasn't got his bike.'

'I am not coming with you, Donald, just go on. If Mina is staying with one of the neighbours, then I'm staying here tonight. I'll sleep here. After all, it's my house now,' he said, smiling down at me.

'It's finished, Craig,' I said determinedly. 'I'm not marrying you. I have just told Alex he can go to Northfield any time, and you are going with him.'

Donald murmured something about looking at his bike and walked out leaving us alone. Craig made to take me in his arms, but I warded him off.

'I mean it, Craig, it's finished. Goodbye.'

I turned to make for the door, to get out of the house and

away from the look of pain and hurt on his face, but in two strides he was at my side and held me to him.

'Don't, Mina. You said that before, remember, and you couldn't do it. You can't do it now,' he pleaded. My eyes, my cheeks and my lips were covered with kisses. 'If you do this to me, there is nothing left for either of us. Your love for me, Mina, is the greatest thing that ever happened to me. My love for you is not something you can throw back, and you know it.' His two strong hands were holding my face up. I had to look at him.

'Mina,' his voice was entreating, beseeching, 'some people can love several times in their lives, others perhaps two or three, but our kind of people only once and this is it. Suppose you leave me, and I leave you, suppose we go our different ways and marry? It will never be love, Mina. Here we belong, together, so let's hear no more of goodbyes.'

I dislodged myself from his grip. 'I'm not marrying you, Craig.' My voice was like a stranger's. 'Help me, Craig. If you really love me, help me now and just go.'

His face had turned white and his hands were shaking as he raised them to his hair, a habit he had when upset. I saw that he realised I really meant it and why.

'Donald,' I called from the door, 'Craig is ready to go.'

Donald entered the kitchen and looked at us both. Perhaps he realised at that moment just how much we loved each other. 'God, Mina,' he said, is there no other way?' I shook my head.

'I will be here after church tomorrow,' Craig said, 'to try to knock some sense into that head of yours. I'm not giving up, and that's that.'

As he passed me, I touched the sleeve of his jacket. Donald nodded to me and passed out. I watched from the window, dry-eyed, as they disappeared round the bend at Mrs McAndrew's. God bless you and keep you, Craig. I whispered into the pane of glass.

I knew exactly what I had to do. I entered the cottage and went into the room where so much had happened to me. Uncle Dunk and Aunt Anne seemed very near. Dry-eyed, I mounted the stairs, picked up my nightdress off the bed and went to Mrs Fraser. She was sitting knitting and her daughter-in-law was making cocoa. Andrew rose and introduced me. I saw a fair-haired pleasant girl with a ready smile. We talked for a little while before they turned in, and I was left alone with Mrs Fraser. Everything I had done until now seemed automatic and even my voice seemed listless and dull as I told my dear friend what had happened. 'You must promise never to reveal my new address to Craig, or I will never write.' I said earnestly.

'I promise,' she said. 'You can rely on me.' I knew that I could and was grateful.

'What are you going to do now, lass?'

'I don't know. I really don't know.'

She rose. 'You are in the spare room, Mina.' She gave my shoulder a gentle squeeze. 'Perhaps things won't look so bad in the morning.'

But things were just the same. I was leaving the Glen forever. I made my way to the Brae House, packed my belongings and looked around for the last time. Then I walked downstairs. Peter arrived and told me to be ready by half past one. I looked at the clock on the mantlepiece. Eleven o'clock. I had two hours. I slipped a light cardigan round my shoulders and made for Tomnaloich. I sat beside the crag where I had met Bell McPhee, and looked about me. The glens and valleys were spread before me, and an eagle soared high above me, heading in the direction of the mountains. The deer grazed lazily a few hundred yards away with the stag standing sentinel over the herd. They were all there, as if they had come to say goodbye. The lapwings and the gulls were flying over the Lochan, as I had seen them so many times before. The heather was coming into full bloom and the blackberries were nearly ready. This, I was leaving forever. The peace and quiet of this scene and the meaning of its wild, rugged beauty, would be with me always. I can see it today, over forty years on.

I descended to the moor below, skirted the Lochan for the last time and bade farewell to the Brae House. I picked up my case and handed it to Peter. I was dry-eyed still, as I left my childhood and my sweetest memories behind. A new chapter of my life had begun, for good or ill.

Chapter 18

The train was tearing down through the Highlands towards Perth. With every turn of the wheels, I was being taken further away from all I loved and cherished and a black cloud of depression swept over me. I could throw myself out of the window, I thought, but I knew that I wouldn't, because I was too much of a coward. Perhaps the train would crash and I would be killed, I thought hopefully. That wouldn't do either.

There were other people travelling and I wished them no harm. So I just sat there, and gazed out of the window, watching the mountains, rivers and lochs flashing past. The dining car attendant came and summoned us to morning coffee, and later, lunch. I still didn't move. If only I could cry. Tears, they say, are a balm to the soul, but tears would not come. Passengers who were in the same carriage passed to and fro at intervals, sometimes glancing at my figure at the door, but passing on. No one spoke. Perhaps they sensed that I wanted solitude.

On arrival at Perth, I changed trains. My destination was to be Pirnhill, the nearest station to Turlum Castle. An hour later, as I stepped off the train at the small station, I was approached by a stocky man, about forty.

'Are you Mina Forbes?' he asked. I nodded.

'My name is Dave Clark. I drive for the Estate Office and I've been asked to pick you up.' The porter was standing with my case which he handed over to Dave. 'The best of luck to you, lass, you will need it going to Turlum Castle.'

'Give over, Jim, don't frighten her off before she gets there.'

It wasn't until we came to Turlum village, about one and half miles away, that I spoke. 'Is this not a good place?' I asked.

Dave Clark hesitated before he said. 'This is the village. Quite a nice place. I live here and most of the Estate Workers live here, although some, naturally, live on the Estate. The Estate Offices are here too.'

I noticed he hadn't answered my question, so I repeated it. Again he hesitated. 'Well, Mina, you see the Gentry are only in residence three months of the year for the Grouse Shoot. The rest of the time they live on their estates in Buckinghamshire or in London. This means, you and the housekeeper live alone for the other nine months of the year in the Castle.'

'What's the housekeeper like?' I asked.

'Well, you saw her at the interview, didn't you?'

What a lot had happened to me since that interview. If I had been asked to describe her, I doubt if I could have done so with any great accuracy. 'I didn't take much notice of her,' I replied quietly.

We left the village behind and a mile further on passed through the huge wrought iron gates with the Moncrieff coat of arms emblazoned across them, and so on up the drive about another two miles to the Castle. As we approached, Dave spoke again. 'A lot of housemaids have passed through Mrs Armstrong's hands. I think the record is three months for a girl to stay.' He gave a short laugh. 'I wonder how long you will be here?'

'You're very cheerful, aren't you? What is the housekeeper really like?'

'Hard as nails,' was the blunt reply, as he drew the van to a stop.

I stepped down just as Mrs Armstrong came out of a side door. Approaching me, she held out her hand. 'Welcome to Turlum. Thank you, Dave,' she said, turning to my driver. I picked up my case. 'Follow me,' said the housekeeper, and entered the castle with me at her heels.

We arrived at what is called the Stillroom, where all the cakes, teas and coffees are made, when the "folk" are in residence. 'I use this as the kitchen and dining room. I do all the cooking. You do the housework, with my help, of course.' Mrs Armstrong explained. 'When the Gentry are in residence, you act as third Housemaid of five. Of course, you already know that. It was discussed at the interview.'

'Sit down at the table,' she ordered. 'The meal is ready. Afterwards I will show you your room.'

I am not going into details about service in High Society because, as I have said before, it has all been written about so many times. But I must write about Mrs Armstrong, because of the influence she had on my life. She was a typical housekeeper of the old school, tall, slim-built and very imposing looking. Black dress down to the calf of her leg with a small lace patch pinned to her greying hair. Keys dangled at her side. It didn't matter whether the Gentry were in residence or not, the work went on. So many rooms in the castle were kept swept and dusted every day. Carpets were lifted and dust sheets spread over the furniture in most of the rooms, especially the public rooms. Most of the bedrooms were just left, but had to be aired and kept clean by Mrs Armstrong and myself.

I could understand why the estate workers and most of the people in the village feared Mrs Armstrong and called her a tyrant. She certainly stood no nonsense from anyone. She expected and gave no quarter. Tradesmen, shopkeepers, even the Estate Factor, did not escape her rough tongue, if the occasion arose. The first two months I was there, I was lonely and often depressed. I told myself a hundred times a day that I would hand in my notice, but I didn't. I had to work hard, from half past seven in the morning till five o'clock at night, with only time off for meal breaks, but it helped my aching heart.

Never a day passed but I could see Craig's face. Over and over, I could see his arms outstretched to receive me. I felt his kisses, I could hear his deep voice telling me of his love. At times, I felt I had had enough. Why suffer like this? I thought, I'll go back to where I belong, to Craig. At other times a calmness would steal over me. You have done the right thing a voice seemed to say. You couldn't drag Craig down to your level. You would never forgive yourself. I would then plunge into my work and try to forget.

When we had finished work for the day, I either knitted, sewed or crocheted. My hands were never idle. Sometimes I walked to the village for Mrs Armstrong on some small errand.

All this, for the first two months, was my life. Sometimes, at meal times, I could see Mrs Armstrong looking at me, but never once did she question me about my past.

I got to know the estate workers' families. They were a friendly lot and asked me to join in their recreations, such as dancing and going to the nearest cinema, which was in the small market town of Milton, three miles from Turlum. As I was allowed only one day off a week, I made my excuses. This didn't stop them from coming to the Castle to see me and invite me to their homes. Mrs Armstrong didn't object to their visits, nor to my going to visit them in my time off.

In this way, I became friendly with the carpenter's daughter, Edith Chalmers, and Rita Lane, the carter's daughter. They both had boyfriends and did everything they could to get me fixed up with a boyfriend as well, but on this I was very adamant, refusing their every effort at matchmaking, which gave the boys on the estate, and in the village, the impression I was standoffish.

Then, suddenly, everything was all go. Word arrived from the Factor's Office that the Earl and Countess were coming on the 1st August for the 'shoot'. Carpenters, joiners, plumbers, bricklayers and electricians descended on the Castle under the eagle eye of the housekeeper. Work went on in perfect rhythm. Every floor in the Castle was scrubbed by an army of chars from the village, under the direction of a Miss McDougall. When they had gone, carpenters laid the carpets, furniture was placed into position, dust sheets were removed and folded by Mrs Armstrong and myself, packed into clothes baskets and despatched by Dave to the laundry. On their return, they were packed away in linen cupboards for future use in November. Furniture was washed and polished until my arms ached. Floors were also polished where there were no carpets. There were not so many fitted carpets in those days, even in large houses. Woodwork was washed, walls were swept down, and the joiners hung the massive curtains. The beds were made up of the finest linen, blankets of the finest wool and the bedspreads were out of this world. Mrs Armstrong gave me a running commentary on where they came from. India, China, Japan and, of course, Britain. All made of the finest materials available.

Then we descended on the staff room. Here too Mrs Armstrong made no difference. The same thoroughness was observed. The last place was the huge kitchen and scullery. The range stretched four yards across the kitchen floor. I had to blacklead it and burnish the steel until it gleamed. This was a mammoth task, as the steel was spread over with oil to preserve it from rust when not in use. This took me a whole day. The cleaners scrubbed the stone floors.

At last, it was finished. Mr Ellis, the Factor, Mrs Armstrong, Dave and myself stood in the massive ballroom. Mr Ellis was speaking.

'Well, Mrs Armstrong, you have surpassed yourself as usual.'

'Thank you, Mr Ellis.'

Dave turned to me smiling. 'That speech between these two is a ritual. It happens every year and on this spot. It's like the coming of the Gentry, an annual event.'

I smiled back and turned to walk away. Dave followed. 'How are you getting on with the old battleaxe anyway?' He asked curiously.

'I'm getting on fine. I rather like her.'

'Well, wonders will never cease,' he said wide-eyed. 'I never in all my twenty years on the Estate heard anyone say that before.'

'That's because you don't know her. It's just a matter of give a dog a bad name.'

Dave looked at me in amazement, but before he could speak, the Factor approached. 'Take me to the office, Clark.'

Chapter 19

The arrival of the Earl and Countess of Moncrieff, along with their family, relations and friends, has little or no bearing on my life. They came and they went, and November found the housekeeper and me once more alone in the Castle. A hectic fortnight

ensued after their departure. The team of male workers arrived
and carpets were rolled in brown paper, dust sheets were
brought out and the furniture covered. Curtains were taken
down, folded and put away. Many of the Public Rooms and
several of the best bedrooms were locked and only opened once
a week to allow me to open the windows in the morning, and the
same in the late afternoon to shut them.

So, when the third week in November came round, Mrs
Armstrong and I were left to caretake. It was as if all those
people had never been.

Chapter 20

Christmas was drawing near when Mrs Armstrong asked me
one morning if I wished a long weekend at New Year. 'I
noticed you didn't bother much about your days off during the
season.'

'I had nowhere to go.' I said.

'You must have relations, surely.'

'No one.'

There was silence for a few minutes. 'Well, I'm going up to
Pitlochry,' said Mrs Armstrong: 'I have two brothers, bachelors,,
up there outside the town. They work a smallholding and I
usually go up about this time for a week and put the house to
rights, and again for a week in summer. If you have nowhere
to go, Miss McDougall will come and stay with you and bring
Rachael with her. You have met Miss McDougall, haven't you?'

'Yes,' I said. 'She was in charge of the scrubbers. But who's
Rachael?'

'Her daughter. She's a mongol, but you don't have to worry.
She won't do you any harm. Miss McDougall cleans the Estate
Offices and comes up here every spring to wash all the blankets.
She just comes in any time she's required and, in exchange, she
has a room and kitchen in the village rent free.'

Miss McDougall duly arrived, and Mrs Armstrong went to
Pitlochry. Rachael was a poor soul. A woman of about forty
with the mind of a child. I was sorry for her, and a little afraid
of her too.

Edith and Rita came to visit me as usual. 'What about going
to Turlum with us to the Hogmanay Dance. It's a great night,'
they told me excitingly.

At first I refused, but Rita, with her persuasive way, made me agree. She was a lovely girl, Rita, with natural wavy, fair hair and laughing blue eyes.

'Well,' I said, 'I'll have to ask Miss McDougall.'

'Her!' Edith grumbled. 'According to my Mum, she was some lady when she was young.' Rita and I laughed at this.

'Come on, we'll go to the stillroom and ask her,' I said.

Miss McDougall had no objection. 'Go and enjoy yourself and tell me all about it tomorrow, but don't wake me up when you come in. Rachael always has a bad day if her sleep is disturbed.' So it was settled.

That night, I dressed myself in a blue velvet dress, brushed my long black hair until it shone, a little lipstick, a dab of powder, and I was ready. I used no beauty aids other than the two items mentioned.

I descended the back stairs and went along the corridor to Mrs Armstrong's sitting room where Miss McDougall was listening to the wireless. Rachael was already in bed. They shared one of the staff rooms. I think it was the room that the fourth and fifth housemaids shared when in residence at the castle, about four doors down from my room.

'My, but you look grand.' she said admiringly. 'What beautiful hair and eyes you have, Mina.' I thanked her. 'Edith and Rita are waiting in the stillroom. Have a good time.'

Edith was dressed in green. You couldn't call Edith beautiful by any means. Her hair was mousey brown, her nose was on the large side, so was her mouth, and her eyes were grey, but if it was a friend you wanted, Edith was the very one. I liked her very much. Rita's dress was pink, and, as I've said before, she was a lovely girl.

As I entered the stillroom, Rita, bubbling over with excitement, told me Tom Fleming was waiting outside. 'He is taking you, Mina. Jim Thompson, as you know, is my boyfriend and Edith is, of course, going with Jack Robertson.' I knew they would be meeting their boyfriends at the hall. The boys belonged to the village and they usually had this arrangement when they went dancing.

I looked from Rita to Edith. Edith nodded. 'Please, don't be annoyed with us. We had to get you a partner. We know you don't know many people and Tom offered to take you.'

Tom Fleming was the son of the Head Gamekeeper, an only child. I knew that neither Mr Fleming, nor his wife, would like the idea of their son going anywhere with a maid from the castle. 'I'm not annoyed, just surprised. Coming?'

We met Tom at the back door. He wasn't a very tall boy. He had red hair and the complexion that went with it, and he would be about twenty, I thought. He smiled at me. 'Hallo. I thought you were never coming. I'm cold standing here.'

'We will soon sort that out,' Rita said and started to run down the drive. Tom took to his heels and followed her, with Edith and me bringing up the rear. Other Estate workers were also on the road, so we all joined up together and arrived at the hall about nine o'clock.

I enjoyed the dance very much. Tom was a good dancer. But I wasn't, never having had the opportunity. 'Just listen to the music and follow me,' were his instructions and I did.

I expected to be a wallflower, being a stranger in a clannish community such as Turlum. But I was mistaken. I got plenty of dancing. At twelve midnight, the New Year was hailed with lots of laughter, handshaking, kissing and bursting of balloons. After that, the dance became rather rough. Rita and Edith came over and asked me to go first footing with them and their boyfriends.

'When will we get home?' I asked.

'Oh, sometime in the small hours,' Edith replied.

Rita giggled. 'Breakfast time, more like. Come on, the men are waiting. Go and get your coat.'

I shook my head. 'Sorry, girls, I can't. Miss McDougall would tell the housekeeper when she comes back and I would get sacked.'

'Och, she'll never know. Come on.' Rita was making for the door as she spoke but Edith held back.

'I see your point, Mina. Tom will take you home when you are ready. Oh, here he comes.'

I turned towards Tom. 'I don't want to spoil your night, you go with the crowd. I'll manage fine by myself. I'm not afraid of the dark.

'Nonsense, I brought you here and I'll take you home. Come, let's dance,' he said.

Edith touched my arm. 'Come up to Mum's tomorrow for your dinner,' and she vanished through the door.

I looked at Tom and saw he had had a good drink. 'Come on, Tom,' I said, 'I'm going home, the dance is getting a bit rough.'

'Good,' he said, 'I hoped you'd say that.'

I got my coat and met him at the door. He put his arm around me and in this fashion we walked through the village and along the main Milton Road towards the big gates. Halfway up the drive he stopped. 'Let's sit here,' he said, throwing his coat on the banking and sitting down.

'What for?' I asked.

'Come here and I'll show you.' He grabbed my hand and before I realised what had happened, I was on my back. His breath was hot and smelled strongly of drink, which disgusted me. His lips were wet as he tried to kiss me and his hands were groping at my clothes.

Terror seized me. 'For God's sake, Tom,' I gasped, 'what do you think you're doing?' I pushed him aside and tried to rise, but he held me down by my hair.

'Isn't this why you didn't go first footing and wanted to leave the dance?' he said smirking. His free hand tore at my clothes again.

'You pig, you filthy pig,' I screamed at him, and with all the strength of healthy youth, freed myself by striking out with arms and feet. I leapt to my feet, but my assailant was just as quick. This time, I was ready and with my hands I tore at his face. His grip loosened.

'You bitch!' I saw him lift his hands to his face.

I ran and ran, crying and limping. I had lost a shoe and also my handbag. Still crying, I arrived at the castle, only to discover the back door key was in my handbag. There were no windows open, of that I was certain, for it was I who had locked them. I would have to waken Miss McDougall now. What if Tom decided to follow me? He had to pass the castle to get home. I imagined I heard his footsteps on the drive. I pulled off my other shoe and ran round the castle to where the staff quarters were. If I can't rouse Miss McDougall, I'll break a window, I thought. But what window? I had no idea. I didn't know the castle that well yet.

Frantic with fear, I threw my shoe at a window on the second floor. The shoe hit the wall and fell some yards away. I couldn't see where. I dared not shout, in case Tom heard. He couldn't be that far away. I groped about for stones and threw them, but it was hopeless. In despair, I picked up one as large as my fist and threw it with all my strength. There was a crash of splintering glass. A moment or two later, a light went on up in the fourth floor to my left.

'Oh, thank God,' I breathed. The window opened. 'Let me in, Miss McDougall,' I sobbed. I heard her say something, that I couldn't catch for I was running back round the castle to the stillroom door. I thought that door would never open. I waited for what seemed an eternity then the fanlight above the door lit up and a moment later the door opened.

What I must have looked like to a woman half-asleep, I don't know. She just stared at me with her mouth open. I knew my hair was all over my face, my coat, minus the belt, was open and my dress was ripped down the front. I was in my stocking soles and my feet were bleeding. I entered the stillroom, sank into a chair and wept.

Miss McDougall never spoke until I was calmer and had stopped crying. She then handed me a cup of tea. 'Drink that and tell me what happened to you.' Between sips of tea I told her, and after I had finished, she sat silent for a moment or two, eyeing me up and down. Then she started to laugh.

'Is that the first time you have been roughed up by a man?' she asked.

'Miss McDougall,' I said hotly, 'he tried to rape me!'

I rose from my chair, took off my coat and tried to tidy my hair. 'Are you suggesting I encouraged him?' I was indignant.

Miss McDougall laughed again. 'Well, you refused to go first footing and wanted to leave the dance early with your escort. What else was he to think? Tom is a lad for the girls, you know. Didn't Rita and Edith tell you?'

I shook my head. In the security of the castle, my fear dropped and rage took its place. I turned on Miss McDougall. 'How would you have liked a man clawing at you and tearing at your clothes, his filthy hands wandering all over your body?'

'At your age,' she said, still laughing, 'I loved it. Many a rough and tumble I had too. Get on with you, Tom wouldn't have raped you. A refusal from you would have been enough, but you got scared, and by the look of you fought like a tigress. I'll bet you scared poor Tom too, in the end.' Her laughter echoed around the stillroom.

'What kind of men, or was it boys, have you been out with, eh?'

I remained silent. Her laughter ceased as she studied me for a moment or two. 'You are a strange girl, Mina, and a very proud one. I would have given a lot to have been like you when I was a girl. I had Rachael when I was your age, and I had enjoyed a few men before that. You will never get a man if you treat them like you did Tom, you know.'

'If you had all these men, why didn't one marry you?' I said cuttingly.

'Oh, I had plenty of offers, but I had Rachael and she came first. No man would accept Rachael. Come on, let's go to bed.'

'I'm sorry,' I said feebly, 'I shouldn't have said that.'

'Och, I've had worse things than that said to me, lassie.'

I felt humiliated. I knew I could never follow Miss McDougall's philosophy, nor live her kind of life. What must Rita and
Edith think of me? I didn't know that if a girl left a dance before
it was finished with a man friend, there was an ulterior motive.
Rita and Edith left before the dance was finished because they
were going first footing to friends' houses in the village. I left
before the dance was finished, . . . and Tom must have thought
. . . ! I squirmed with shame. I had learned a lesson I would
never forget.

All men were not gentlemen and all girls were not what they
seemed to be either. In my ignorance, I had believed the world a
different place to what it was. What a fool I was! Oh, I heard
plenty of talk in the staff rooms and learned many things about
sex there, but everything just brushed past me.

Next day I remained in the castle, but that night Rita and
Edith called to ask why I didn't go to Edith's for dinner.
Instead of answering, I asked 'Have you seen Tom Fleming?'

Rita was the first to speak. 'Oh yes, tell us what happened,
Mina. His face was all scratched. Oh, tell us Mina,' she asked
eagerly.

Edith spoke up. 'Perhaps Mina doesn't wish to discuss it.'

'I wish to discuss it all right,' I flung at them. 'Why didn't
you tell me what he was like? I was never so humiliated in all
my life. You both knew what he was like, yet you allowed me to
go to the dance with him, and worse than that, you allowed me
to come home with him. Why didn't you warn me?'

Both girls remained silent and looked at each other. Rita was
the first to speak again. 'You made an awful mess of his face,
Mina. Why didn't you just tell him to buzz off? That's what we
tell our boyfriends when they start their nonsense. Don't we
Edith?'

I stared at both girls, speechless. I felt I had been brought up
in an entirely different world, which in a sense, I had. At
Inverleith House, when off duty, I was accompanied by a
senior member of the staff, as I was considered a minor and not
allowed dates. Not that I wanted any. I had Craig. But this was
different. I was on my own and I felt my two friends thought me
a fool at not being able to hold Tom off, instead of tearing at his
face.

Rita tittered. 'I bet Tom Fleming will watch where he puts
his hands in future.'

We all laughed at this and I felt better.

Chapter 21

Two days later, Miss McDougall and Rachael left for home and Dave Clark brought Mrs Armstrong back from Pitlochry. Life went on as usual. If Mrs Armstrong ever knew about my escapade with Tom, she never mentioned it, but I had no doubt that she would hear all about it. There were plenty of people on the Estate to tell her. Besides, the window had to be put back in and my shoe and handbag were handed in by an estate worker.

The following July, we were back at square one. The Earl and Countess were coming up for the shoot again, bringing with them their staff, relations and friends. The staff who had come up from England the previous year were amazed to see me still there. 'How can you stick the old battleaxe?' they would say. 'It takes us all our time to stick her for three months, and you have been here over a year!'

How indeed? I didn't know myself. I just knew exactly what was expected of me and did it. I got to know when to speak and when to remain silent and, most important of all, I got to know the woman as well as the housekeeper. Perhaps she was a hard taskmaster, but I discovered she was a very just one. I was never asked to do something she couldn't do herself. I was never interfered with as long as I did my work and did it to her satisfaction.

The time came for the Gentry to return to England and I discovered I was glad that Mrs Armstrong and I were going to be left again as caretakers of the Castle. Another Christmas was drawing near and I knew Mrs Armstrong would be going to Pitlochry soon.

One evening, we were both sitting at the fire in her sitting room. I was knitting a cardigan for Edith for her Christmas. I had already finished Rita's and Mrs Armstrong was doing her books. She had to keep account of everything we ate and all the cleaning materials we used. Bills from the shopkeepers in Milton had to be checked before going to the Estate Office for payment. I waited until she put down her pen, put the books into her desk and locked it.

'Mrs Armstrong, when are you going on your holidays?' I asked.

'When you come back from yours,' was the reply.

'You know I have nowhere to go,' I said quietly. 'I will just have them as I did last year, a day here and there, coming back here at night.'

'You have never told me anything about yourself, Mina, not that it's my business. You do your work well. You are honest and trustworthy and I have no complaints, but I know absolutely nothing about you.'

'There is nothing to tell,' I said. 'I was brought up by two elderly people up North. They are both dead now.'

'Were you born up there?'

'No. I was born in Aberdeen and boarded out.'

There was silence.

'Mina, I think a great deal happened to you in the North. I saw it in your face and eyes the first time I saw you. There is a sadness and seriousness in your expression that should never be there in so young a girl. You should be laughing and gay and wanting the company of girls and boys your own age. Instead you seldom go out unless Edith and Rita call and make you go . . .'

I didn't really hear the rest of her sentence. I was far away. I could see Uncle Dunk sitting on his chair. I was remembering the kindness and love he gave me. I could see Craig and feel his love, like a mantle wrapped around me, warm and secure. How I loved these two men. All I had wanted was to be loved by them, but this was not to be. Uncle Dunk was dead, and Craig . . . well, that was my own doing. I couldn't turn the clock back now.

'Mina,' Mrs Armstrong's voice was firm, 'did you hear me?'

I rose and laid down my knitting on the chair. 'Yes, Madam,' I said, looking at her.

She saw the tears in my eyes and instantly turned away. 'I'm sorry, Mina, I didn't mean to pry.'

'That's all right, Madam.'

'Go and make the supper. I'll be in directly to give you a hand with the tray,' she said kindly.

It was after New Year, when Mrs Armstrong had returned from holiday, that she suggested I get in touch with the Authorities in Aberdeen to find out who I really belonged to. At first, I wasn't interested, but on giving it a great deal of thought, I asked Mrs Armstrong one morning at breakfast how I would go about it.

'Well, first I think you should write to City Hall, giving your name and age, where you were brought up and by whom.'

This I did, and a week later I received a reply. It was from a Mr Wilson, a Councillor from an office in Union Terrace, asking me to call there and ask for him and he would give me all the help he could.

'There you are,' Mrs Armstrong said, after I had given her the letter to read. 'The Authorities aren't so bad after all.'

'I don't know,' I said, uncertain, 'it is very blunt and to the point.'

'All business letters are like that, Mina. What did you want Mr Wilson to do? Write you a love letter?'

I smiled as I took the letter back. 'I'll make arrangements for you to go to Aberdeen,' Mrs Armstrong said.

'Couldn't you come with me?' I asked.

'Well,' she hesitated. 'It would need to be done in one day. We both can't leave the Castle, even for one night. One of us must be here, but if we left early in the morning and Dave Clark took us to Perth Station and collected us at night we might just make it. I'll find out about trains and make arrangements with the Factor for Dave's services.'

So, a fortnight later, we arrived in Aberdeen, the city where I was born. Mrs Armstrong hailed a taxi at the station to take us to Union Terrace. I stepped out of the taxi, gazed at the building and childish fear came back. This was where my Birth Certificate was and a dossier with my name and progress over the years when I was under the care of my foster parents. Here I would find out who I was. The Authorities were now going to condescend to enlighten me.

'Come, Mina,' Mrs Armstrong's strong voice broke into my thoughts, 'Let's go in.' We walked up the steps and entered through the swing doors. A large counter spanned the length of the large hall. As we approached the counter, a girl rose and asked us politely if she could help us.

'We have an appointment with Mr Wilson at ten o'clock,' Mrs Armstrong said.

The girl asked us to wait a moment and disappeared through a door behind the counter. While we waited, I looked around. The floor was covered with beautiful mosaic tiles. The counter was mahogany and very highly polished. On the walls were large life-size pictures of past Councillors, Magistrates and all the others officials who made up the 'Authorities' as the boarded-out children called them. I supposed every big town had a place like that. What I didn't stop to think, was that we would have been very poor creatures indeed without them.

The girl returned and asked us to follow her, leading us into a big office, brightly lit by large windows which took up one side of the wall. As we entered, a man rose from a swivel chair.

He held out his hand to Mrs Armstrong and asked her to be seated in a comfortable chair opposite him. Then he turned to me and I instantly recognised him as one of the men who had come up to the Glen every two or three years to see me. As he held out his hand, I saw he recognised me too. I ignored his hand, and, without permission, sat down beside Mrs Armstrong, and looked at him across the wide desk.

He coughed nervously and, looking at Mrs Armstrong, said, 'I am Mr Wilson.'

Mrs Armstrong nodded. 'Thank you for giving us your time.' Then turning to me she said, 'Well, Mina, you know why you are here. This is your affair.'

Her voice was the typical voice of the madam I knew so well. You are here to do a job, so get on with it. I was on my own. I wasn't getting any help from her. I looked across again at the man behind the desk. He was older than I remembered. The reddish fair hair was now white, but his bearing was as formidable as ever.

I rose, came over to the edge of the desk and stood looking down at him. My fear of him and all he stood for dropped from me like a cloak.

'Who am I?' I asked in a clear, firm voice.

'Well now, you are Williamina Forbes, aren't you?' He rose and went over to a filing cabinet. 'Let see how. Mmmm...D, E, F, that's right. F. for Forbes. Here we are. Sit down, Williamina, and we will see what's in here.'

I remained on my feet. As he looked up at me his eyes wandered all over my body. 'I remember you as a very tiny girl, Williamina, three or four years old, I think, the first time I saw you. I said then you would be a beauty some day, and I'm not far wrong.'

I felt a hot flush rise to my cheeks. I turned and took my seat beside Mrs Armstrong. Mr Wilson turned to my file again. 'I haven't got your Birth Certificate here, you will get that at the Registry Department. I am giving you the address of an Aunt of yours.' And he handed over a piece of paper. 'If you go there, you will receive all the information you need. She knows you are coming, and I've ordered a taxi for you. I think it will be here now.'

He rose. So did Mrs Armstrong. 'Thank you, Mr Wilson. Come, Mina.' She held out her hand. I just sat there.

'Mr Wilson,' my voice was slowly rising in anger at this man's condescending manner. 'It's my parents I am enquiring about, not my Aunt.'

'I know nothing about your parents, Williamina. It was your Aunt who put you into the care of the Parish. It's her name and address we have on your file. The address I gave you.' He opened the door for Mrs Armstrong.

I rose from my chair and swept past him. I was making for the outside door when he stopped me. 'Williamina, don't blame us. We do what we think is best for a child. We didn't ask for you to be brought into our care, you were sent to us.' He paused. 'I would like you to come back and see me again, when you are in a different frame of mind.'

I nodded briefly and walked out. Mrs Armstrong was in the taxi when I got in. 'Well,' Mrs Armstrong said, 'what's the address?' Without looking at it, I handed it over.

'Mrs W. MacIntosh,' she read aloud. And to the driver, '260 Woodside Terrace, Kittybrewster.'

The driver nodded and as the taxi moved away, the house-keeper turned to me. 'You know, Mina, I don't know what to make of you. I know this is your affair, and I don't want to interfere. You are also off duty, which makes it difficult for me, but I do wish you wouldn't be so standoffish. Please, try and relax yourself.'

I couldn't answer. What could I say? Mrs Armstrong was trying to help me find my place in society, help me to belong and I was grateful. I turned and smiled at her. 'Please don't be angry with me,' I said simply. She grunted and we both remained silent for the rest of the journey. When our taxi stopped we were outside a bungalow. Mrs Armstrong turned to pay the driver. 'That's all right, Madam,' he said, 'Mr Wilson paid it.' And he moved away, leaving us on the pavement.

As we approached the door, it was thrown open by an elderly woman, about fifty, who invited us in. After she got our coats off in the hall, we were escorted into a large and spacious sitting room. The elderly woman turned to me. 'I am your Aunt Kate, and you are Mina, or is it Wilma?'

'I get called Mina,' I said, warming to this homely woman. She was tall and rather stout, her hair had once been jet black but was now greying at the temples. I looked into her hazel eyes, so like my own, and liked what I saw. I introduced Mrs Armstrong and explained who she was. As we sat in the sitting room, I told my new Aunt Kate of my foster parents and of my upbringing. I felt I had come to a house of kindness and love. It was a long, long time since I had felt like this.

As we were talking, a young girl came in. 'This is your cousin Vera, my youngest,' Aunt Kate explained. Another girl entered just behind Vera. 'And this is Eva. I think she is a year younger than you. You will see Jack, my eldest later. He is at his work just now.'

As I shook hands with my two cousins, I thought they didn't look like sisters. Eva was fair, whereas Vera was like her mother, very dark.

Eva said dinner was ready and we were asked to join them at table. As we sat down, a man about Aunt Kate's age came in. 'Hallo, everyone,' he said cheerfully.

'This is your Uncle Willie, Mina.' I rose and shook hands.

'My, but you are like our Vera. Isn't she Kate?'

Aunt Kate, instead of answering, introduced Mrs Armstrong. The dinner was delicious and I enjoyed it very much. My cousins took me upstairs to their bedroom and showed me photos of the family.

'Who is that?' I asked, as a small woman appeared in quite a lot of the photos.

'That's Aunt Ann, you will like her. She is coming round later to meet you. She is an old spinster, very prim and proper and all that, but we love her. Her home is in Ardarroch Place.'

'I think you have a beautiful home here,' I said.

'Oh, it's all right,' said Vera, 'you should see my pal's home, much nicer than this.' I envied my cousins their way of life, the security they had and the love of their parents. 'Do you know about my mother and father?' I asked, wondering when they were going to talk to me seriously.

'Oh, they are both dead, I think,' Vera said. 'We are all you've got, and Aunt Ann, of course. That's on your mother's side. We don't know about your father's side. Mum will likely tell you.'

We were called downstairs half an hour later to the sitting room. Uncle Willie offered to take Mrs Armstrong out to see his garden, which he seemed to be very proud of. Aunt Kate told the two girls to go with their father. 'Oh Mum, must we?' Vera said woefully.

'Yes,' Aunt Kate said firmly. 'I wish to talk to Mina.'

After they went, I turned to my Aunt. 'Vera tells me my parents are both dead.'

'She would,' Aunt said. 'Vera is the talkative one. Yes, they are.'

'Was my mother your sister?'

She nodded. 'Yes.'

'And my father, who was he?' She looked at me for a few moments. 'His name was Forbes.' She hesitated. 'Mina, why don't you accept us as your parents? Why rake up the past?'

'It was you who boarded me out. Why?' I asked, determined to find out more.

'Well, I couldn't keep you,' she said. 'I brought you out of the Maternity and intended to keep you, but we were so poor at that time. Your Uncle Willie hadn't finished his apprenticeship as an Engineer, and we already had Jack. We intended you for adoption, so that you would get a good home. When we went back to the Orphanage, you had been boarded out to a family in Aboyne. We were told you were very happy there and the family discussed adoption. I don't really know what happened, but after three years, we were told you were back in the Orphanage. By that time, I had Eva and couldn't possibly take you. I had no room in the first place. I lived at that time in Shore Place, in one room, so the parish decided you should be boarded out again.' She looked at me and as I made no move to speak, she carried on.

'Six months later, your Uncle Willie had a bad accident at work and hurt his back. He was in hospital for three months. He could never go back to his old job, and as it was a Government contract he was working on when the accident happened, he was compensated. This is when we bought this house. After we had settled here, I made enquiries about you at Union Terrace, only to be told you were boarded out again, up North somewhere. They thought it best that way.' She rose from the chair. 'Well, Mina, that's the whole story and here you are, and welcome home.'

As I rose, she put her arms round me and gave me a kiss. At that moment the door opened and a tall young policeman entered. 'Hello, Mum, have you something nice to eat? I'm starving. You must be Wilma,' he said turning to me.

His mother planked a kiss on his cheek. 'Not Wilma, Jack, Mina.'

'Oh that's a nicer name,' and he shook hands with me. I could see he was like his Dad and I could see his Mum doted on him.

'This is my son Jack, Mina. He is in the police force, as you can see. I'm afraid I'm going to lose him soon. He is going into the American force and leaves sometime this year. Excuse me, lass, while I give this lad something to eat.'

When Uncle Willie came in with Mrs Armstrong some minutes later, conversation became general. On Aunt Kate's return from the kitchen, Mrs Armstrong asked if Aunt Kate thought it a good idea for me to stay on a few days, to get to know my new relations.

'I'm glad you mentioned that, Mrs Armstrong. We will all be delighted.'

'It was your husband's idea and as Mina hasn't really had a proper holiday for some time, I have given my consent. You will return on Saturday then, Mina,' she said, turning to me.

'Thank you Mrs Armstrong, but I have no nightclothes.'

'Don't worry your head about that,' Aunt Kate broke in, 'Eva is about your size and she has plenty.' So it was settled. When Mrs Armstrong left by taxi for the station and my two cousins were discussing plans for my entertainment, the door opened.

'That will be Aunt Ann,' said Jack, as he rose to open the sitting room door.

I was sitting at the window with Eva and Vera when I turned. Did I imagine what I saw, or did Aunt Kate really shake her head and did a look of relief pass over Aunt Ann's face. I just had a fleeting glimpse of their faces at that moment, so I couldn't be sure. But I was to remember it later.

Aunt Ann wasn't tall, but she was very neat, beautifully dressed and groomed from her auburn hair to her neat shoes. I don't know if that was the true colour of her hair or if it was tinted. She certainly wasn't like homely Aunt Kate. Her interest in me was nil, or so I thought, so it wasn't long before I turned my attention once more back to my cousins.

I enjoyed every moment of my holidays. I was made a fuss of by Aunt Kate and Uncle Willie and was entertained to the full by my cousins. Jack wasn't always with us because of his police duties. We danced, went to the theatre and pictures and when it was time to leave, I was sorry.

'Well,' Aunt Kate said, 'you can sort that out. Why don't you come and live here? You could get a job like the girls in a shop, and this could be your home.'

I hesitated before I spoke. 'I would love to very much, but can I get to know you all a bit better first?'

'Of course, you can, my dear,' Aunt Kate said warmly. 'We are all going to miss you, so hurry back.'

Chapter 22

So it was back to Turlum Castle and work. I didn't mind as much as I thought I would. I felt more contented, knowing I now had someone who belonged to me and that I belonged to them. Letters passed between me and the girls every other week, with snatches of gossip and what we were doing and where we were going.

Then spring arrived, and Edith came down to the Castle with a ticket to a dance in the village hall in aid of some charity or other. Rita was now engaged to her boyfriend and would be going with him, but Edith and her boyfriend had split up, so I decided to go with her for company. After asking the House-keeper, of course! In service, a maid like myself never did any-thing except her work, without asking either a Head House-maid or Housekeeper. If the request was refused, there was no discussion. One didn't ask the reason why, one just accepted in silence. If permission was granted, a slight bow of the head and a quiet thanks sufficed. Mrs Armstrong seldom refused me a request, possibly because I didn't ask for many.

So Edith and I went to the dance. As we came out of the cloakroom and entered the dance hall, the band was playing a slow foxtrot. I glanced around the floor and my heart nearly stopped beating. At first glance, I thought I was looking at Craig McKenzie. I sat down on the nearest chair and asked Edith as she sat down beside me, 'Who is that chap dancing with Margaret Chisholm?' I knew Margaret quite well. Her father was a forester on the Estate.

Edith looked round, 'Oh, yes,' she said, and then after a few moments, 'That's Bill Southall.'

At that minute the dance finished and Bob Fisher came over to speak to Edith. He was a bricklayer whom I knew quite well, having seen him up at the Castle. I knew he was fond of Edith, and now she was free, he obviously wished to become her boyfriend.

'Are you dancing, Edith?' he asked.

'Yes, Bob, but first Mina wants to meet Bill Southall.'

'I don't, Edith,' I said quickly.

'Yes, you do,' she said. Bob laughed and called over to where Bill was standing. But when he came over and I saw him at close quarters, I realised that he wasn't like Craig at all, only his hair and the shape of his head were alike. 'Meet my pal,' Bob said. 'Bill, meet Mina Forbes.'

We shook hands, after which Bob and Edith disappeared among the dancers, leaving me feeling terribly embarrassed, but when Bill spoke and asked me if I would like to dance or sit this one out, I felt more at ease. His voice was soft and gentle, there was no mockery in his blue eyes, and I liked the way he looked me straight in the eye. He was as tall as Craig but slimmer built. No, he wasn't like Craig at all, I decided.

'I don't dance very well,' I said smiling.

'Neither do I, so that makes two of us.' He only said that to put me at ease because he was a beautiful dancer.

I didn't see him again until the dance was nearly finished when he came over. 'This is an Eightsome Reel,' he said, 'so come on and let's have some fun.' Edith and Bob were also in the set.

When the dance was finished, he asked if he could take me home.

'Do you know where I live?' I asked.

'Yes,' he replied, 'Bob told me. Turlum Castle. You are the maid there, aren't you? Bob is taking Edith home.'

'Oh I am glad. Bob has been trying hard to date Edith.'

'Well, you won't want to play gooseberry, so what about me taking you home?' he asked.

I immediately hesitated. I already had had one experience of a young man taking me home. 'I don't know,' I said timidly.

Edith and Bob joined us just then. 'This is the last dance, Mina,' she said.

'Bill has asked to take me home,' I said quickly.

Edith looked at me and knew what I was thinking. 'Bill is a gentleman, Mina. Honest,' she said, as Bob drew her on to the dance floor.

Bill was a gentleman in every sense of the word and the longer I got to know him, the better I liked him. Our names were soon coupled together as Bob and Edith's, but with me, I had no intention of feeling anything serious. How could I? I could never love him. I liked him, yes. But love, no. Several times I tried to explain to Bill that I didn't wish to become involved. 'Neither do I,' he replied, 'so just let's carry on until one of us meets the right one.'

He was easy to get on with. I didn't have to explain myself to him. If I didn't wish to see him for a week or two, he accepted it. When I wished to see him, there he was. This went on for several months.

The Earl and Countess had come and gone again and we were finished cleaning the Castle after their departure. I hadn't seen much of Bill during the season apart from an odd evening out, but he was delighted at the departure of the gentry, for it meant that he could, on invitation from the Housekeeper, come up to supper with me once a week after his work.

It was on one of those November evenings, after he had left, that Mrs Armstrong spoke to me about him. 'Bill is in love with you, Mina. I hope you aren't going to hurt him. He's a very nice boy.'

I stared at her in surprise. She had at no time spoken of Bill except to say that I had her permission to have him in to supper. 'Bill Southall,' she had said, 'Oh yes, he is of a very respectable family. His mother has a small farm, about sixty acres I think, on the other side of Pirnhill Station. Yes, you may bring him in to meet me.'

'I think you are mistaken, Madam,' I said, coming back to the present.

'No, I'm not mistaken,' she replied. 'I know you don't love him, that is obvious, so why not call it a day and let him look around for someone who isn't just looking for a friend to pay them into the pictures and the dancing, as you are. The longer you go on like this,' she continued, 'the harder it is going to be on Bill when he does propose, as he will, and then be brutally turned down by you.'

'I wouldn't hurt Bill, Mrs Armstrong. He is far too nice,' I said quickly.

'No? Then what are you hanging on to him for?'

'I'm not. We have an understanding that we will pal about together until the right one comes along and then go our separate ways.'

She looked at me for a long time while I felt my face getting redder and redder.

'You,' she said, looking straight at me, 'met Mr Right a long time ago, Mina. Bill met Miss Right when he met you. Don't hurt him, Mina. You know what it's like to be hurt. Now, I'm going to bed. Goodnight.' And with that she left the room.

Next day, something happened that put Bill completely out of my mind. I was busy in the library dusting the hundreds of books that were shelved there. I liked that part of my work, for I loved books and had read a great deal of them, with the permission of Madam, of course, and a stern warning to put them back exactly where I found them. *A Tale of Two Cities* by Dickens was my favourite. Daphne Du Maurier's *Rebecca* was another and, of course, *Wuthering Heights* by Emily Bronte. I had just picked up a book by A. J. Cronin when Mrs Armstrong came in. 'There is a young man at the stillroom door wishing to speak to you,' she said.

'Who is it?' I asked, without much curiosity.

'He said his name is McKenzie.'

My hand flew to my throat. I felt I was choking, but it was

only the rapid pounding of my heart. My first thought was that Mrs Fraser must have told. And she had promised me she wouldn't tell Craig where I was. The blood rushed to my cheeks and my knees as if they would buckle under me. Mrs Armstrong was still standing at the door, watching me.

'Tell him to call back when your work is done and have tea with us.' She turned on her heels and walked away, disapproval written all over her face.

I walked along the two corridors towards the still room, my heart still thumping madly. But when I opened the door, it wasn't Craig. It was Donald.

My anger rose as I saw him standing in the middle of the floor. 'What do you want and how did you find me?' I said, all in one breath.

'Well, well, what a warm welcome after three years.' He held out his hand. 'How are you, Mina? It is three years, isn't it?'

I ignored his hand. 'What do you want?' I repeated.

'I don't think that ogre likes me either,' he said, meaning Mrs Armstrong. 'She left me standing at the door when she went to get you, so I stepped inside.'

'You can just step outside again then,' I said. 'I am not allowed visitors during working hours.'

I felt he was laughing at me. He was smiling, but his smile didn't reach his eyes. 'You are losing your Highland accent, Mina,' he said. 'You will have to come back to the Glen to pick it up.'

Mrs Armstrong's voice came from behind me. 'Introduce me to your friend, Mina, please.' This I did and I noticed how she eyed Donald up and down. 'My maid has work to do, Mr McKenzie. Why don't you come back this evening?'·

'I will just do that,' he said. 'In the meantime, I'll book in at that hotel I saw as I passed through the village. The Commercial I think it was called.' He smiled at me and left.

As Mrs Armstrong and I sat down to tea about five thirty, I was very quiet. I was dreading the return of Donald, yet I wanted him back. I wanted to hear about Craig and I wanted to hear about the Glen.

'Mina,' Mrs Armstrong's voice was firm. 'Who is Donald McKenzie, and what is he to you?'

'He is absolutely nothing to me. He was related to my foster parents. At least his mother was. She was their cousin.'

Mrs Armstrong remained silent. I felt she was due some explanation, but I couldn't tell her about Craig. 'Possibly

Donald was in the vicinty and just decided to look me up.' I
went on.

'He must be quite well off to afford to stay in a Hotel, even
for a night. Especially the Commercial. And I see he has a
small car,' Mrs Armstrong said. In those days, few people had
cars and few people could afford to stay in hotels. Certainly
not the people in my walk of life.

'Oh, I didn't know he had a car. It was a motorbike the last
time I saw him.'

Mrs Armstrong rose from the table. 'You can have an hour or
two to see him, Mina, but be in by ten. I am now going to the
sitting room.'

When she had left me I washed the dishes, tidied myself, then
went to my room, and after picking up my coat that was lying
over a chair, I went out to meet Donald. He was waiting outside
the Castle and as I approached, the car door opened. 'Like it,'
he said proudly.

I stepped in and sat beside him. 'Well, not knowing anything
about cars, I don't know, but it seems quite nice,' I said.

'Where will we go?' he asked.

'Can't we stay here?'

'Stay here, in front of a hundred windows,' he laughed,
'don't be silly.'

'Well, let's go down the drive then,' I said.

We drove down to the gates and Donald parked the car under
one of the huge oak trees at the side of the drive. 'I got this little
beauty in Inverness yesterday. Wait until I get home. They will
be surprised.'

'How is your mother?' I asked, for something to say.

'Fine, and so are John and Jean. But you don't want to hear
about them, do you, Mina. It's Craig you want to hear about.'

'How did you find me, Donald?'

'Mr Fraser told me. His wife died a fortnight ago. She had
your address.'

'Mrs Fraser dead!' I whispered. 'Oh, I am sorry.' I felt
terrible. I thought she had given away my secret and I was
wrong.

'I was at the funeral,' Donald went on. 'Mr Fraser is going to
Inverness to stay with one of his sons. As I was leaving, he asked
me to let you know about his wife, and as I didn't know your
address, he gave it to me. So, here I am.'

He put his arm over the back of the seat. 'You didn't have to
come here to tell me about Mrs Fraser, Donald,' I said quietly.

'No, I didn't. I have come to ask you to marry me, Mina.'

'Sorry, Donald, I could never do that, and you know it.'

'Why not?' he asked. 'You would be mistress of Drumoich. Mother says that when I get married she will go to the Brae House.'

I laughed. 'Yes, but if you told her it was me you were going to make mistress of Drumoich, that would be a different story.'

'It would have nothing to do with her,' he said stubbornly.

'Sorry, Donald, it would be impossible. Turn the car round and take me back.'

'You don't mean that, Mina. You want to know all about Craig before I take you back,' he said with a leer. His arm came over my shoulder and he tried to draw me to him. I remained as stiff as a poker.

'Open the car door, Donald,' I said.

'Mina, I love you and want to marry you. Don't you understand? I want to see you in Drumoich, as my wife. I have pictured it so often, and when I got your whereabouts from Mr Fraser, I couldn't believe my luck. You know what passed through my mind, Mina? Wait until Craig hears about this lot.'

I turned round and faced him. 'You don't love me, Donald. You want me at Drumoich to spite Craig. Well, just you go back to Drumoich, and when Craig visits you there, tell him I still love him and will always love him.' Anger and rage were tearing me away inside. I wanted to hurt him and felt that I could gladly have killed him. I tried to choke back the sobs that rose in my throat, but couldn't. I felt that I mustn't let him see me like this and, turning away, I fumbled blindly at the handle of the car door.

'All right, Mina,' he said at last, 'I'll take you back. I have never taken a girl against her will. Not yet anyway.' He laughed harshly, then said 'Craig isn't married yet, Mina. Isn't that what you wanted to hear?'

Yes, oh yes, that's what I wanted to hear, I thought. 'How is he, Donald?'

'Fighting a losing battle with the farm. We are in a deep depression in this country and it has struck at agriculture as well as everything else.'

I knew about world depression and the mass of unemployed, but it didn't touch me. I was a servant, and as such, was always in demand.

We arrived at the Castle and, as Donald drew the car to a standstill, he turned to me. 'Mina, he is killing himself trying to pay off the debt without having to marry Elizabeth Leitch. I've told him it's hopeless. Alex is getting married soon and wants a place of his own. Well, that's about all. Except that my offer still stands.'

I shook my head and stepped out of the car. He was at my side in an instant. 'Who do you think you are, turning my offer down? Some high and mighty Miss? Well you're not, you know. You are only a skivvy, so come off your high horse and don't be a fool.'

My eyes blazed into his. 'That's right, Donald. I'm only a skivvy and that is what you want at Drumoich. You would keep reminding me and I would never be allowed to forget it, married to you. No thank you, Donald. Goodnight and good-bye.'

I hurried towards the stillroom door, heard him mutter something about being a bitch, but I never turned as I opened the door. I heard the engine of his car start and, as I shut the door, I came face to face with the housekeeper, who rambled on about being fifteen minutes late, about disobedience, and so on. I stood until the tirade stopped, then slipped past her to my room. It was there, for the first time since leaving the Glen, three years before, that I broke down and wept, and wept.

Next day, the housekeeper came into one of the rooms where I was working, disapproval written all over her face. 'Really, Mina, this is too much. That young man is back again. I told him you couldn't see him until your work was finished, so he is coming up this evening. I am not allowing you out every night like this. I don't approve.'

That was obvious, but I had the sense to remain silent. She turned to the door. 'I told him six o'clock. For one hour.'

I met Donald outside the stillroom door. He came out of the car as I approached. 'Hop in,' he said, 'and we will go for a spin.'

'Donald,' I said calmly, 'I said goodbye to you last night, remember? Why are you still here?'

'Aha, hop in and I'll tell you.'

'I've only an hour, the housekeeper . . .'

'To hell with the housekeeper.'

'But my job . . .'

'And to hell with your job. Get in,' he almost shouted.

There was something here I didn't like. Donald entered the car, opened the door at the other side for me and I took my seat beside him.

'Look, Donald, don't go far. I must not be more than one hour.'

Donald never answered, but accelerated down the drive.

Where we went I don't remember, because he talked all the time and what he was saying made me freeze inside. 'I have been speaking to a maid in the hotel where I stay. Mabel her name is. Know her?'

I remained silent, but I knew Mabel who went to the village dances. Her second name was Thorpe, I think. She considered herself one of the best dancers in the hall and, as Bill Southall was also considered a splendid dancer, she resented his attentions to me and to my friends who, in her opinion, were not in the same class as herself when it came to dancing. I had no doubt this was true, as Edith had told me about her resentment and dislike for me, but I had no idea what was coming next.

'I see you do know her,' Donald said. 'Your silence is enough. Who is Bill Southall?' he asked, after a pause.

'Just someone I know. You can't stay in a place as long as I have and not know some of the people.'

'Well, according to Mabel, this Bill has a younger brother, Angus, who has been talking about his big brother Bill and a young girl called Mina Forbes. He had a few drinks one night in the bar of the hotel and was telling his pals that Bill was going to ask Mina Forbes to meet his Mum soon, then get engaged at Christmas. What do you think of that, eh?' he asked smugly. 'Craig would love that story.'

I sat perfectly still in my seat beside him. The only sound was the purring of the car. I looked at Donald. He was watching me out of the corner of his eye, a smirk of triumph on his face.

'Stop the car,' my voice was quiet and steady. The car drew to a halt at the side of the road. 'Donald,' I turned and looked at him. 'I don't know what is in Bill Southall's mind, and if I've been asked to meet his mother and then become engaged at Christmas, it is unknown to me. Edith, my friend, her boy-friend Bob Fisher, who pals with Bill Southall, and I, make up a foursome. That's all.'

Donald laughed. 'You are not going to tell me that there is a platonic friendship between you and a man, Mina. That, I will never believe. The very thought of it makes me laugh.' He threw back his head and roared with laughter. 'There is no man could look at you, Mina, and think of a platonic friendship.'

He got out of the car and came round, opened the door at my side and asked me to step out. 'It's a lovely moonlight night. Let's walk.'

My hour was long since up and the rage of Mrs Armstrong wouldn't get any worse with an extra hour late than with ten minutes late. We walked along the road and Donald put his arms around me. I stopped and went rigid. As I did so, I noticed that Donald's face went white and that his hands shook. 'You don't have to act like that.'

I stepped back. At that moment I was afraid of him. I don't know why, but I was. Turning, I walked back to the car and sat down. A minute or two later Donald entered and drove away but as the car gathered speed, I felt even more afraid and gripped the edge of my seat. I was thankful when we turned in at the Castle gates and he had to slow down, as it was all uphill. In those days, cars were not as powerful as they are today, at least, not the smaller ones. As he drew to a halt, he turned, and his voice was as cold as steel. 'I am returning tomorrow to the Glen. Craig will be delighted at all the news I have to give him.'

'You do what you like, Donald,' I said.

'A man,' he said, ignoring my remark, 'is never so insulted as when a woman freezes at his touch.'

'Donald, I didn't mean to insult you, but can't you understand that there is only one man for me? Your brother. Please, let's part friends.' I opened the door and stepped out, then turned and held out my hand. He ignored it.

'The next time we meet, you won't get off so lightly,' he said threateningly.

'There won't be a next time, Donald.'

'Ha, that's what you think.' The door was slammed shut and the car roared down the drive.

The next time I saw Donald was to be in very different circumstances.

I walked towards the Castle knowing what was facing me. Mrs Armstrong's wrath. I was hours late.

Chapter 23

It was over a week after Donald had left that I met Bill by accident in the village. 'Hallo, Mina, where have you been hiding yourself?' he asked, coming out of the paper shop. As he stood looking down at me, a newspaper in his hand, I suddenly felt embarrassed.

'What's wrong, Mina?' he asked, in his quiet gentle voice, as we started to walk away from the village.

'Nothing, nothing at all,' I said, trying to keep my voice normal.

'There is. What is it?'

'Well, if you must know, Mrs Armstrong has forbidden me to see my friends at the Castle or at their homes. I'm being kept in. No days off, or evenings either. I stayed out late one night and I still have another week to go. If she sees you with me, that will be another row. And no boyfriends either,' I added.

'When will I see you then?'

'Bill, I don't think we should see each other again.'

'Why not?' he asked, surprised.

'Well . . .'. I hesitated. It's not as if we were serious about each other or anything like that.'

We had left the main road and were crossing the Deer Park as it was called. This cut out the long walk up the drive and came out at the summer-house beside the tennis-court. Bill stopped and put his hand on my arm. 'But I'm serious, Mina, dead serious.' I've found you, Mina, and I don't want to look any further,' he said quietly. 'I was coming up tonight to see you and to tell you that.'

But when I reached the Castle and told Mrs Armstrong that I had met Bill and that he was coming up tonight, she said, 'Well, you won't leave the stillroom. And I'll be in the sitting room. You are certainly not getting out, and when Miss McDougall arrives up tomorrow, I'll give her my instructions concerning you. You have still another week before you get time off.'

'What if Miss McDougall can't come up? What if Rachael isn't well?' I asked. 'You know sometimes she doesn't keep the best of health.'

'Don't be an ass,' Mrs Armstrong rapped out. 'It's her job to convenience me.

Bill arrived after tea. I met him at the stillroom door and invited him in. Mrs Armstrong wished him good evening. 'Mina isn't going out, Bill,' she said, 'but I have no objection to you talking to her in here. I'm going to the sitting room to do some writing. I'll see you before you go away.' That meant Bill could stay until she returned. As she shut the door behind her, I asked Bill to take a seat. 'She's not very pleased with you, Mina,' he said, nodding towards the closed door and smiling at me.

'You shouldn't be here,' I said, sitting down.

'I want you to come with me to The Mains on your next evening off. I would like you to meet my mother and my brother Angus.'

I looked at Bill for a moment. 'So I gathered,' I replied, 'and you also want me to become engaged to you at Christmas.'

Poor Bill. He just sat there, staring at me. 'Your brother was in the Commercial Bar one evening,' I went on, 'and had too much to drink and started talking.'

'Angus! When I get home . . .'

'You will do nothing when you get home.' I interrupted. 'It's not his fault that I know what you discussed with your mother. He didn't mean any harm. It was the person who discussed it with me who meant the harm.'

'It doesn't matter. Let's forget it.'

The anger left his face, but hurt took its place. I saw it in his eyes. I turned away. What was it Mrs Armstrong had said? 'Don't hurt Bill Southall, as you have been hurt.' And I had just done that.

Without speaking, Bill went over to the chair and picked up his coat and made for the door. His hand was on the handle when I spoke.

'Bill, come back.' Those three words were to change my whole life. Why did I call him back? I don't know. I didn't love him, I didn't even want him as a boyfriend, much less a husband, but I liked and respected him. I didn't see him throw his coat back on the chair. I only heard the rattle of the buttons on the wood as it landed there. I felt his arms around me and I could smell the Harris Tweed of his jacket.

After he kissed me full on the mouth, he held me at arms length and looked into my eyes. 'Mina,' he said quietly, 'if I had walked through that door, I would never have come back. I don't know what would have happened to me then, because without you, there would be nothing. You see, I love you, very much.'

He spoke calmly and without passion. What Bill said, he meant. He wasn't demonstrative, never that. He just has his own way, quietly and gently.

'You will come and meet mother and Angus then?' I nodded. Happiness flooded his face. 'I won't wait for old Eagle-eye to come through, so when will I see you?'

'Come up Saturday night. Miss McDougall will be here as Mrs Armstrong is going on holiday.'

When Bill had gone, I went up to my room. I didn't want to talk to Mrs Armstrong just then. I must have time to think. I sank on to the chair beside my bed and stared at the blank wall. My thoughts wandered back to the Glen and to Craig. The Lochan would be frozen over by this time, I thought. I could see myself screwing my skates onto my boots and skating over the black ice. Suddenly, a terrible homesickness washed over me and an awful longing for the Glen. It was like a cancer inside me, deep down in the pit of my stomach. Then, there was Craig. Why did I have to love him the way I did? What kind of person was I anyway, that could feel so deeply? I just didn't seem to be able to separate Craig and the Glen from my mind. Perhaps that was why I called Bill back tonight. Deep inside, I knew Bill loved me the way Craig did.

When I entered the sitting room five minutes later, Mrs Armstrong had already poured the tea. I lifted my cup and was sipping the hot liquid when she spoke. 'What was Bill saying to you tonight?'

'Nothing,' I replied.

'He took a long time to say nothing and you don't usually rush away to your room after your visitors go.'

'Are you all packed, Madam?' I asked politely, changing the subject.

She rose from her chair. I could hear her keys jangling at her side. 'Wash the dishes and tidy up,' she said curtly. 'See to all the lights. I'm going up now. Goodnight.' I knew she wasn't pleased with me for not discussing Bill's visit with her, but I just couldn't, not tonight.

Chapter 24

Kate McDougall arrived with Rachael next day and while she and the housekeeper were closeted in the sitting room, Rachael followed me through the Castle. I was no longer afraid of her. We had come to know each other very well, poor deformed creature and I often wondered what went on in her mind. I also wondered what would happen to her when her mother died. She would be put into a home very likely and kept out of sight, in case she offended society by her presence or showed it up for its shortcomings in coping with people like herself.

When Mrs Armstrong had left, Miss McDougall made tea and we sat in the stillroom. I had come to like the old char, and behind her rough exterior I think she had more common sense than many a person with more education and polish. Towards the end of her stay, I asked her what Bill's mother was like. Kate knew everyone for miles around, their parents and grand-parents before them.

'Teen Southall? Oh she is all right. Had a hard life. Lost her

man when she was only thirty seven. Her brother-in-law had to
come down from Dornoch and work the place until Bill was old
enough to leave school. But she's no Sassenach. She belongs to
the village.'

'Not a Sassenach, Miss·McDougall,' I laughed. 'That's what
we call an Englishman. You mean a Teuchtar.'

'He came from up there. You know what the highland folk
are like. They don't like dancing or enjoying themselves like us.
They don't even have an organ in their churches.'

'They are not like that at all, Miss McDougall,' I said. 'At
least, not all of them.'

'Well, you should know.'

I remained silent. Miss McDougall, like a lot more people had
a very distorted idea of the Highlands and its people. That was
due to the lack of communication and travel.

'So that's the way the wind is blowing is it?' she said, looking
at me out of the corner of her eye.

'It doesn't mean I'm going to marry Bill, just because I'm
meeting his mother,' I said hotly.

'That's exactly what it will mean to Bill,' was her quick remark.

Mrs Armstrong returned the following Saturday. The next
day was to be my first evening out for three weeks. Young people
today would not tolerate this state of affairs—being penalised
for coming in late and so on—but this was pre-1939 and the
system demanded unquestioned obedience from those who
served. There were two choices, knuckle down, or get out. So
when Bill called that evening, it was with a sigh of relief that I
left the Castle at his side.

We walked in silence through the village and on to the
station road. About half a mile past Pirnhill Station, we turned
off the road and on to a cart track. 'We don't have far to go now,'
Bill said. 'The Mains is just round that corner.'

'This doesn't mean, Bill, that we will get engaged or anything
like that.'

He took one of my hands in his, and with his other hand
pushed a wisp of hair back from my face, looking me straight
in the eye. I looked down towards the ground. 'No, Mina, I will
never ask anything of you that you can't give.' he said softly,
and holding my hand we went towards the cottage.

I liked Bill's mother on sight, a woman in her late forties with
a good firm handshake. She was certainly an outdoor type. Her
weatherbeaten face told me that, although it was not from
choice. I also liked her warm welcome. 'Take off your coat and
make yourself at home.'

Just as I was about to sit, Angus, Bill's brother walked in.
I thought for a moment Bill had a twin, so alike were they. The
only difference I could see was that Angus wasn't so tall, but
they were both very like their mother. After supper, Bill and
Angus went out to the steading and I was left with their mother.
'They have done that deliberately, she said. 'I asked them to.
I want to get to know you without the boys around.' She handed
me a dishcloth. 'Bill is very fond of you, Mina.'

I remained silent. 'All I've got is the two boys,' she carried on,
'and when they marry, I hope I will like their wives. I like you,
Mina, so that's not a bad start,' she smiled.

As I dried the dishes with her, I knew I could get on well with
this woman. She said what she meant, and meant what she said.
I could see why I liked Bill so much. He was extremely fond of
his mother and that is not a bad thing in any man.

We left about nine o'clock, as I had promised to go back early.
It wasn't until we were crossing the Deer Park that I mentioned
his mother. 'Your Mum is a very nice person, Bill.'

'I could see you got on fine together,' he said. 'It's a pity its
this time of year, but when the spring comes, you will see The
Mains better. It's lovely up there.'

I didn't answer. As we approached the Castle, Bill drew me
over and we perched on the parapet. Turlum Castle was built
on a rock and where we sat was a sheer drop of about forty feet.
'We have five minutes,' he said putting his arm round me.

I jumped down onto my feet. In a flash he was standing in
front of me. 'You're not afraid of me, Mina, are you?'

'Of course not, Bill.'

'Well, why do you either walk away or just stand like a statue
when I put my arms around you?' he said quietly, his voice
sounded hurt. He lifted my chin up with his hand. 'I love you,
Mina,' he said simply, 'You love me too, don't you.'

'I'm terribly fond of you, Bill,' I said.

'That's enough for me. I'll see you on Friday at the dance. Do
you want me to come to the Castle?'

'No, I'll meet you in the hall. I'll likely go down with Edith
and Rita.'

I told Mrs Armstrong about my visit over a cup of cocoa
before going to bed. She listened, and waited until I finished.
'He is a very nice young man, Mina, and too good for you.'

I stared at her. 'What do you mean, Madam,' I asked
indignantly.

'You don't care for him, Mina, and you're only making a fool
of him.'

I rose from the chair. 'I'll clear the table and wash up,' I said, trying to hold on to my temper.

'That's right, Mina, you do that. Run away from the truth. You don't deserve a man like Bill, you deserve someone like that young Ronald, or whatever his name is that came down from the Glen, and I certainly didn't think much of him.'

I had gathered up the dishes and put them on the tray while Mrs Armstrong was talking, but when I went to lift the tray, I discovered I couldn't. My hands were shaking. Whatever happened, I had to keep my temper. A housemaid didn't lose her temper with the housekeeper no matter what, and I had been trained in a good school. My voice, when I spoke, though shaking, was still under control. 'Madam, the young man's name you are speaking of is Donald, not Ronald, and you are mistaken in thinking he means anything to me.'

'Well, what did he come here for, if there was nothing between you?'

'He was looking for a housekeeper, Madam, and hoped I'd take the job.' This time, I managed to lift the tray and made for the door.

'Mina.' Her voice had the ring of authority that I knew so well when she was angry. I turned and faced her, the tray between us. 'You are treading on dangerous ground, talking to me in that haughty manner. Just be careful.'

She swept past me. The rattle of her keys at her waist and the swish of her dress spoke volumes.

Chapter 25

Perhaps I would never have gone to live with Aunt Kate in Aberdeen, if it hadn't been for an episode about a fortnight after Rita's wedding.

I received a letter from Mary McAndrew in Rothesay. It had been sent to Inverleith Hall and re-directed to Turlum. Mary didn't know where I was and wanted to find out before the third of August as she was getting married then and wanted me as her bridesmaid. But what really made my heart sing was the sentence, 'I am getting married in the Glen in the Wee Free Church and the reception will be at my home in Balgreig.'

I ran into the stillroom to Mrs Armstrong. 'I'm invited to a wedding in the Glen.' The words came out in a rush. 'I'm to be the bridesmaid.'

She looked at me. 'I haven't called you for your breakfast yet, Mina. You are supposed to be cleaning out the fire in the sitting room.'

I turned to go. 'I'm sorry.'

'Don't bother going back now, sit down, it's ready.'

I washed my hands and sat at the table. When we had finished, Mrs Armstrong brought up the subject of the letter. I took out the page where I was invited and handed it over. There was silence for a minute or two as she read the page and, after handing it back, she said, 'Do you see the date of the wedding?'

'Yes,' I said, 'the third of August. What about it?'

'The Earl and Countess arrive on the tenth for the shoot. Before that it's the cleaning of the Castle. I'm afraid you will need to send your apologies. You can't go.'

'Can't go!'

I stared at the housekeeper.

This woman was daft. I had been waiting for an opportunity to return to the Glen since the day I had left it. The opportunity had come and I was grasping it with both hands. No housekeeper, not Earl nor Countess, grouse shoot or pheasant shoot was going to stop me. I rose and took the page out of her hand.

'I'm going, whether you like it or not.'

I spoke slowly and deliberately, so that what I said would sink in. Just as deliberately, I folded the page, put it into the envelope, then started to clear the table.

Mrs Armstrong rose. 'Put down those dishes and listen to what I have to say.' I put the dishes back on the table and waited for her to speak. 'Do you realise the consequences of what you have just said?'

'Yes, Madam, and I'll save you the trouble of saying what you are going to say. I wish you to take my notice, as from now.'

'Very well, you can now get on with your work. I take it it's a month's notice.'

'Yes.'

But it was three nights later before I saw Bill. The moment I met him at the bottom of the drive, I knew he had been told. The maid at the Castle was leaving after three years. The Factor at the Estate Office and his staff had to be informed by Mrs Armstrong, so it was no secret.

'Is it true you are leaving?' were his first words. I told him I was. 'What happened?'

As briefly as possible, I told him that too. 'And what about us, Mina?' he said, when I had finished.

Here was my chance to tell him I neither wanted to become engaged nor to marry him. But I couldn't. I was too much of a coward. After I'd left for Aberdeen, perhaps he would meet someone else, I thought, then there would be no need for me to hurt him.

'Aberdeen isn't so far away,' was my only answer.

Mrs Armstrong and I had little to say to each other, except where it concerned our work and on the fifth of April, I left Turlum. I had no regrets except for my friends, and Bill. Especially Bill. I felt very sorry for the way I was treating him. We had made an arrangement that he would come up in about a month's time. As a plate layer on the railway he received free passes so, for him, travel was cheap.

Chapter 26

Aunt Kate and Uncle Willie and my cousins were delighted to have me. Aunt Kate said I didn't need to get a job right away, but could take a week or two to rest. But three days later, I saw in the Situations Vacant column of the evening paper that a stillroom maid was required at the Palace Hotel. I showed the paper to Aunt Kate.

'That is the biggest and most expensive Hotel in town,' she said.

'Well, I'm going to see about it first thing in the morning.'

At ten o'clock the next morning I presented myself at the staff entrance. A porter took me to the lift and handed me over to a pageboy. 'The Staff Manager's room,' he said as I entered the lift. He looked me up and down as the lift started to move. 'Looking for a job?'

'Yes, I am,' I replied politely.

'What kind of job?'

'Stillroom maid.'

'Oh.'

'Do you think I'll get it?' I asked, looking down at this fourteen year old boy, with the smart uniform and pillbox hat stuck on the side of his head.

'Well,' he looked me over again. 'You are not a bad looker, and old Withers likes good lookers about the Hotel.'

The lift stopped and the doors opened. 'Who is old Withers?' I asked.

'Staff Manager, Silly. Go straight along the corridor, fourth on your right.'

Mr Withers didn't exactly come up to the description of the pageboy as old. He wouldn't be more than forty and came straight to the point. Name, address, what I did, where I had been, etc. When everything had been taken down on paper, he sat back on his chair. 'We pay £1 per week, board free. You can live in or out. You will have a different day off every week, and when it comes to your day off on a Saturday, you get Saturday, Sunday, and Monday. Anything you wish to know?'

I stared at Mr Withers and wondered if I was dreaming. The pay I was getting was more than double what I had been getting in private service. The time off was unbelievably generous. At least it was to me.

'When can you start?' Mr Withers asked.

'Do you want references?' I asked quietly.

He shook his head. 'I am a good judge of character or I wouldn't be sitting here now, interviewing you. When can you start?' he repeated.

'Tomorrow,' I said.

He rose. 'Six o'clock tomorrow morning then. Come, I'll show you the stillroom and introduce you.'

The stillroom was huge. Hot plates ten yards long spanned the whole length of the floor. Underfoot was a thick green runner-like substance. Three women were on their hands and knees scrubbing. 'Careful you don't slip on the wet floor,' Mr Withers warned. 'The reason the rubber is so thick is to deaden all sound reaching the dining room, over there.'

I couldn't see the actual dining room, but I certainly saw the six swing doors leading into it. An occasional waiter would come out to shout an order to about half a dozen women and girls. On the right side of the room, there were three big urns. Mr Withers took me over and pointed to each in turn. 'Tea urn, coffee urn and boiling water urn.'

About two yards in front of the urns a counter stood at right angles, quite near the swing doors. A waiter stood at one side of the stillroom, maids at the other. Mr Withers indicated with his hand saying 'these are the hatches that come up from the kitchens in the basement,' I counted six. 'When the food arrives on the hatches, it is immediately removed and put on to the hot plates. Come and meet Agnes.'

Agnes Jenkins was the Head Stillroom maid, a stoutish

woman of about forty. She smiled a greeting and shook my hand.

'Is there anything you wish to ask me?' Mr Withers rapped out.

I was silent for a moment, then took the bull by the horns. 'I'm invited to a wedding on the 3rd of August up in Inverness-shire. Can I go? I know I won't be due a holiday, but it's very important to me.'

He looked at me. 'If you are suitable and still here, yes, you can go.' He turned and strode across the large expanse of rubber floor and was gone.

I turned to Agnes. I was terribly hot, as I still had my coat on and what with the hot plates and the urns, the temperature must have been in the eighties. 'I've never been in a place like this,' I said.

Agnes stared at me. 'Come with me.'

At the far end of the counter away from the boiling urns, was a door which Agnes opened, leading into a smaller room. Several chairs, a table and what looked like a locker were the entire furnishings. 'This is my sitting room, where I have my meals. I don't go to the Staff Hall. Did I hear you right just now, when you said you hadn't seen anything like this?'

I nodded. 'Yes, you did.'

'What did Mr Withers say your name was?'

'Mina,' I replied, 'Mina Forbes.'

'Well, Mina Forbes, did Mr Withers not tell you what position you were to hold here?'

'Yes, he did. I'm to be a stillroom maid. I learn quickly and won't be long learning the job.'

She stared at me for a moment and then burst out laughing. 'In a month's time, you are to be the Head Stillroom Maid. I'm leaving to get married.'

Now it was my turn to stare. 'Oh, I didn't know that. Mr Withers didn't say anything about a Head Stillroom Maid.' We both just stood there, eyeing each other up. On the impulse of the moment I added, 'But with your help Agnes, I'll do it.'

'I bet you will too, and I'll give you all the help I can. Anyone who can ask old Withers for time off before they start a job, deserves to get on.'

I loved working in the Palace Hotel. The atmosphere was relaxed and friendly. There were over a hundred of a staff, but I never got to know them all. There were about thirty chamber-maids and I came to know some of them and all the waiters as I came into contact with them every day. I also knew all the kitchen staff, especially the chefs. Six came up from the kitchen every day to supervise the meals.

Everything went like clockwork. At five minutes to nine every morning, a bell rang inside one of the hatches. This was our cue that the breakfast was on the road up. The hatches were opened by the girls who worked with me. All the food was in large steel trays about two inches deep and just over half a yard in length. Some contained bacon, some sausages and, of course, eggs all arranged in different trays. It was all there.

The trays, on arrival, were immediately removed and put onto the hot plates. The kitchen staff were all at work, but the chefs did not come at breakfast time. The swing doors from the dining room would open and the waiters, with their tail coats and white dickies, white cloths draped over their arm and a silver tray in their hand came in. Some of them went to the hot plates and others towards our counter. About a hundred coffee pots, hot water jugs and teapots were arrayed along the full length of the counter. By ten o'clock there were few left.

The dirty dishes started to return about nine thirty. At the far end of the stillroom, away from the hot plates and our counter, were six large sinks. Six dishwashers were employed for this job. The dishes were washed and dried and stacked on racks above their heads for further use. When the girls weren't washing dishes, they were scrubbing the huge stillroom floor. The only difference to this routine was at lunch and dinner, when the young boys, who were learning to be chefs and who dished out the breakfast, were replaced by the chefs who had finished their training. I never saw the Head Chef, nor the Head Pastry Chef, the Big Chiefs, as we called them.

My boss was the Head Waiter, a very dignified and quiet gentleman. As well as having the reponsibility for the dining room, he also had the reponsibility for the stillroom. All the time I worked there, I never heard him raise his voice. When I got to know him I asked one day. 'How do you keep so calm, Mr Gold?'

'I have a good staff, Mina, so there is no need to raise my voice. I am very fortunate.'

When I was on early shift, six o'clock until two o'clock, I slept in the hotel. When on backshift, two o'clock until ten, I slept at Woodside Terrace with Aunt Kate. After ten o'clock, the night porters took over the stillroom, unless there was a big function on. If there was, the backshift remained until midnight.

So time passed, quickly and happily. On my first long weekend off, Bill came up to see me. Aunt Kate and Uncle Willie liked him on sight, so did my cousins.

But Aunt Ann, for some reason or other, didn't seem to care for Bill.

He had gone back on Sunday in order to start his work next day. I still had Monday off and decided to go to Aunt Ann's on the Monday evening. I had an open invitation to her home, as my cousins had. Eva and Vera went often, but I very seldom went. It was just a feeling I had that I couldn't define.

As she opened the door to my ring and saw me standing there, she showed no pleasure, but neither did she show displeasure. 'Oh, come in. I'm just making myself a meal,' she said.

She was a manageress in a large gown shop in the city, but Aunt Kate had told me she had once worked in a factory. Her home was like herself, neat and trim. 'I'm not long in from my work. There was a deficiency in the till and I couldn't leave until I found out what was wrong.'

'Is everything all right now?' I asked, making polite conversation.

'Of course,' she said in a matter of fact voice.

I felt a fool. I shouldn't have asked and should have known that Aunt Ann would never, never leave a job unfinished.

'Would you care for something to eat?' She was carrying a tray from the kitchen into the sitting room.

'No thanks, a cup of tea will do fine.'

'Well, do you mind if I eat something? I'll make the tea later. 'There's the evening paper in the paper-rack beside your chair, or would you prefer the wireless?'

I lifted the paper, wishing I had never come and had gone instead with Vera and her pal to the pictures.

'Your young man away?' she asked, between mouthfuls.

'Yes, he had to go back yesterday.'

'Humph, Kate seems to like him. Can't say I do much.'

I looked at her over the newspaper. 'Why not?' I asked, surprised.

'Well,' she hesitated. 'He isn't good enough for you. What can he offer you?'

I laid the newspaper down on my lap and stared at her in utter amazement. This woman, who had never once given me any indication that she ever gave me a second thought, was now telling me that she thought Bill wasn't good enough for me. Before I had time to answer her, she rose, picked up the tray from her small table and going towards the kitchen said, 'I'll make tea now.'

I wasn't angry. I was too taken aback. I thought, Poor soul, she has had to work all her life for the things she has now, her comfortable home, her beautiful clothes, so naturally she is measuring life by her bank balance.'

When she returned with the tea, I said, 'If you knew Bill, you wouldn't say that. Whoever married Bill Southall perhaps won't have the worldly goods you speak of, but she will have something else, Aunt Ann. His devotion and love.'

'Love,' she scoffed, 'there is no such thing as love. It's only a word. And remember this, Mina, you are old enough to be told. There is only one thing in a man's mind, when it comes to a woman and that is to get her between the sheets, and if he can't get her without marriage, then marriage it is.'

The cup was halfway to my lips and, in sheer astonishment, I let it clatter back onto the saucer. Well . . . I . . . I . . .'

'You must have been very badly hurt at one time to speak like that.'

'Rubbish,' she rapped out. 'You are a young girl and I only want to warn you that there are some queer characters going about.'

I wasn't satisfied with her explanation, so when I got home I asked Aunt Kate. 'Did Aunt Ann have a boyfriend when she was young?'

There was dead silence. Uncle Willie, smoking his pipe, stared at his wife. Eva and Vera, sitting on the settee, started to giggle. I thought Aunt Kate hadn't heard what I said, and was about to repeat the question when she lifted her eyes from her knitting. 'Your Aunt Ann, like any young girl would likely have had friends, some boys among them no doubt.'

'I don't mean that, I mean a special boyfriend.'

'Well, not that it's any of your business, Mina, but there was a special boy. They went together for a while, but it all fell through. Anything else Miss Inquisitive?'

'I didn't mean to be inquisitive,' I said, 'but it's just something she said that made me wonder.'

'Well, I think it's time you three girls wondered about your beds, especially you, Mina. You are on early shift tomorrow.'

Chapter 27

The time had come for me to ask Mr Withers to keep his promise and allow me to go to Mary McAndrew's wedding. I had seen little of the Staff Manager since starting three months ago. I told Mr Gold that I wished to see Mr Withers.

'Nothing wrong, I hope,' he said.

'No, Mr Gold, it's a private matter.'

Next morning at ten o'clock I was sent for to the Staff Manager's office. 'You wished to see me?' Mr Withers asked, after asking me to take a seat.

'Yes. I wish to get off duty for a few days before the 3rd of August.'

I didn't think he would remember me asking him to get off for the wedding, but to my surprise he did. 'Oh yes, Mina Forbes, isn't it? Well, let's see.'

He started looking through papers on his desk. 'Here it is— your progress since you've been here. I see you haven't taken a day off for four weeks.'

'That's correct sir.'

'Why not?'

'I hoped, if I forfeited my days off, you would add them on to my weekend off when the time came for the wedding.'

He sat back on his chair, looked at me and smiled. 'Who put you up to that, Mina?'

'Agnes,' I said, 'before she left.'

'I thought so, she knew all the tricks. Well, you have done very well since you've been here. What's more, you tackled a job you never did before and tackled it very well. Mr Gold thinks highly of you.' He sat up again, looked at a large calendar on the wall. 'Right, you can go on the 29th of July, returning on the 5th of August.'

'Thank you sir.' I was overjoyed. I was going back to the Glen.

'Right then, that will be all.' As I reached the door he said, 'They tell me they have found a monster up there. You'd better watch when you're passing the loch that it doesn't jump out and pull you in. We need you back here.'

Chapter 28

The train arrived at Inverness at five o'clock and on the platform I saw Peter McAndrew. He spotted me about the same time and hurried over to help with my case. I was so happy to see him that when we shook hands, I kissed him on the cheek.

'Oh, can I return that?' he asked laughing. 'How are you, Mina? Although I needn't ask. You look great.'

'What have you got there?' he asked, taking a package I was carrying.

'It's Mary's wedding present. A tea set.' He took it from me and laid it carefully beside my case. We mounted his motorbike and were off.

I drank in all the beauty of the Glen, as the bike ate up the miles. It hadn't changed a bit and a lump came to my throat as I looked at it. When we arrived at Balgreig, I slipped off the bike and gazed all around. Tomnaloich was the first thing that caught my eye. The heather was turning purple on the higher slopes while the bracken on the lower slopes was still green. The Balmacan forest to my left, was as beautiful as ever. I could see the gable end of the Brae House. All I had to do was walk a few yards and I would see it all, but my hostess was waiting with her daughter at the back door to welcome me. We embraced warmly and Mary dragged me in by the hand. 'Dad, here's Mina.'

Mr McAndrew came forward to shake hands. His hair was a little greyer, but otherwise he hadn't changed much, neither had Mrs McAndrew. A woman approached from the parlour door.

'Nan,' Mary said excitedly, 'here's Mina. Hasn't she changed?' So, this was Nan.

I wondered as she approached me what I ever saw in her to be afraid of, or in her mother for that matter, but as long as I was under this roof, and for Mary's sake, I would be polite and do what was expected of me. Nan was thirty two years old now and, I could see, set in her ways. The makings of an early middle-aged woman, stout, like her mother, her hair cut short but without style. I shook hands. 'How are you, Nan?'

'How are you, Mina? You certainly have changed. I would never have recognised the little orphan girl whose clothes and boots were always too big for her.'

My anger rose, but I checked it and smiling sweetly said, 'You have certainly not changed one bit, Nan.'

'Come on everyone, sit in.' It was Mrs McAndrew. 'We were bringing supper forward a little tonight, as we will have a lot to talk about later. The wedding plans have to be finished, and your bridesmaid's dress will have to be altered a little, I'm afraid, Mina. We didn't think you would be so slim.'

We all sat down and grace was said. 'Who is making my dress?' I asked.

'I am,' said Nan. 'Also the bride's.'

'Oh.' I didn't know what else to say.

'Nan is a tailoress to trade you know,' her mother said proudly.

'Oh yes.' I would never have known, looking at Nan's clothes. I began to wonder what my dress was going to be like, as I was by this time very fashion conscious, not only in my dress, but my hair too, and I saw Mary was the same. Her hair was darker than I remembered it, but she had the same laughing eyes, full of mischief, like the time she dared me to ride Jess, the mare. We looked at each other across the table and smiled, both remembering our childhood together.

I was helping Mary to clear the table after our meal when Mrs McAndrew's voice pulled me up with a jolt. 'If you are going out, Peter,' I heard her say, 'take Mina's case to the Brae House.'

The Brae House? I looked at Mary.

'Did you not know, Mina? Meg McKenzie lives there now and when she heard you were coming, she asked if you could stay with her. Don't you keep in touch? I thought you knew.'

'Can I go now, Mary?'

'Of course you can, Mina. Mum,' Mary shouted, 'Mina is going to the Brae House now.'

'What? Now? But I thought . . .'

'Tomorrow will do,' Mary broke in.

'Goodnight, Mrs McAndrew. Sorry, but I must get to the Brae House.'

She must have sensed my feelings as she stepped aside to let me pass. Once outside I ran. I ran and ran and didn't stop running until I got to the door. I didn't even knock, I just turned the brass handle that I knew so well and opened the kitchen door.

Chapter 29

Mrs McKenzie was sitting where my Uncle Dunk had sat, only on a different chair. She was a little greyer and a little older. I didn't speak, but when she saw me, she half rose, then sat down again. Her mouth opened as if to say something, but instead, she opened her arms to me. Her action was so like Craig's. I threw myself down beside her and laid my head on her breast.

She was stroking my hair and crooning. 'O lassie, lassie. Has it been that bad?' Her voice was full of emotion. 'Come, sit down beside me. See, I've kept your old stool. Here it is, behind my chair. Don't kneel to me, Lassachan.'

I rose, wiped my eyes and drew my stool round the chair as I had done so often with Uncle Dunk. I sat down and stared into the peat fire. I could smell its fragrance. The furniture had changed, but the flour and oatmeal kist still sat in the corner beside the dresser with the two water pails on top. Instead of the bare flagstones, there was linoleum on the floor. The window was draped with lovely lace curtains and linen blinds. Instead of being white-washed, the walls were papered. It was cosier, more comfortable, but just the same to me.

'Meg,' I said, taking her hand in mine. 'Craig? Tell me about Craig.'

'Craig is married, Mina, three months ago. He isn't happy, I can see it in his face. He doesn't say anything, but I know. I'm his mother.'

'Northfield is safe then?' I asked.

'I suppose so, but he never speaks about it. Alex was saying when he was over, last week, that there are terrible rows. He is getting fed up.'

Craig's marriage didn't bother me, because I knew, married or single, he loved only me. Then I heard footsteps on the gravel path. 'Someone's coming,' I said.

'Yes, I know,' Meg said, 'I told him you . . .'

I never heard the end of that sentence, because framed in the doorway was Craig.

There was no need for how do you do's. There was no need for speech at all.

I forgot his mother was sitting looking at us. All I saw was Craig, his eyes full of love and his arms outstretched. I threw my arms round his neck, while his closed like a vice round my body and held me there. We still hadn't spoken or kissed, but after a while his grip loosened and he held me away from him. 'Let me look at you,' he said softly.

I had dreamt of this for four long, long years. I threw my arms around his neck again. 'Craig,' I whispered. I lifted my face and he covered me with kisses. He let me go and taking my hand, went over beside his mother and planked a kiss on her cheek. 'Thanks, Mum, for telling me.'

Meg rose from her chair, shaking her head. 'I never thought I would live to see the day when I would be encouraging one of my sons to break his marriage vows. God forgive me.'

'There is nothing to forgive,' said Craig. 'Come on, Mina, let's go.'

Meg looked surprised. 'Where are you both going?'

We looked at each other and smiled.

'I don't understand,' she said quietly. 'I just don't understand. I've been watching you both, since you came in, Craig.' She looked at Craig and then at me. 'It's this wild love you have for each other that frightens me. No good can come of it.'

We both laughed and made for the door. Then we headed towards the moor and the Lochan. It was I who broke the silence, for no word had passed between us since leaving the Brae House. 'It's beautiful and it's wonderful to be back.'

'Let's go up Tomnaloich,' said Craig, pressing my hand.

We followed the paths made by the hill sheep and the deer until we came to the patch of green where Bell McPhee and I had sat, several years ago. 'Stop here please, Craig,' I said, 'This is my favourite spot.'

I turned towards the west, then shading my eyes from the setting sun with my hand, I looked down at the Lochan. Craig was standing behind me with his hands on my shoulders, the last rays of the sun were striking the water, making it look as if there were a million diamonds sparkling there, and I could feel the peace and quietness surrounding me, bringing with it a contentment I had not known for four years, contentment I could never ever feel anywhere else but here.

'Come back to me, Mina,' said Craig, breaking into my thoughts and swinging me round. Then he put his hand behind my head and pressed me to his breast.

'I'm only thinking of the beauty and contentment that's surrounding us,' I said quietly.

He sat down and drew me down beside him where I nestled contentedly in his arms. 'What did you mean just now, when you said "come back to me"?'

'I have a rival, I'm afraid.' he said, stroking my hair. 'Yes, Mina, a rival. The Glen.'

I laughed happily. 'It's true,' he said. 'I felt for one awful moment, as you stood with your back to me, you were just not with me.'

'I'm with you now, Craig,' I said, kissing him on the lips. His strong arms were around me, holding me close to him. 'Mina, I love you and I desperately want you.'

'I want you too Craig,' I whispered.

His voice was deep with emotion as he said. 'Until our love is brought to a climax, we will never know peace. You know that as well as I do.'

I was lying on my back and he was bending over me. 'Yes, Craig, I know, but not here.' His grasp loosened, and I sat up. The sun had set and it was getting dark. 'Craig, if we bring our love to a climax, here and now, I could never leave the Glen.' He sat up beside me and was about to speak, but I put my fingers to his lips. 'Hear me out, Craig, please.'

'Do you know why, Craig? Once I gave myself to you, it wouldn't stop there. Oh no. The craving inside us for each other would go on and on. We would never be happy with a "hole in the corner" affair, it would need to be open and above board, without our names being bandied from one end of the Glen to the other. That wouldn't bother me for myself, I am only an orphan, brought up on the parish by foster parents. But it would bother me for your sake. I love you too much to drag you down to my level.'

Craig sat silent for a minute or two, as if weighing up all I said. 'Will you listen to what I have to say now?' I nodded.

'Four years ago, Mina, you walked out of my life. Relatives, friends and neighbours all agreed it was best that way. I could now get on with my job of building up Northfield, they said. They told me that you, Mina, did the right thing. I would get over it. Time would sort that out.'

'Well, I never got over it. There was never a day passed but I thought of you and wanted you. I willed you to come back to me. I knew you would return some day. I was as sure of that as night follows day. I married Liz Leitch for the sake of Northfield. Poor Liz, if she had any illusions before marriage, she has none now. You are there between us, all the time. What kind of marriage is that?'

'And you are telling me you don't want me to be dragged down to your level. Good God, Mina, you have more breeding in your little finger than all the women in the Glen put together. Stay at the Brae House. Don't go back. It's your home. I want to hear no more of this nonsense about dragging me down.' He rose and helped me up. 'I am staying at the Brae House tonight.'

'Does your mother know?' I asked quietly.

'Yes, I asked her to make up a bed for me in one of the attics. When I knew you were coming, I also asked mother to invite you to stay with her.' He paused. 'Sleep with me tonight, Mina,' he asked.

We were halfway down the hill by this time and inside I kept repeating 'Why not? Why not?' But I remained silent. It wasn't until we were skirting the Lochan hand in hand that I spoke. 'Craig, help me, please help me. Don't tempt me, for it would be so easy to do as you ask.'

We stood at the edge of the water. I could hear the water lapping gently against the side of the bank. He put both hands on my shoulder. 'You are not leaving me this time, Mina. When I heard you were coming to Mary's wedding, I made up my mind then and, like you, I know if you give yourself to me you will never go away. Come on, let's go home.'

Chapter 30

We arrived at the Brae House and as we entered, a cheery voice said, 'Hallo, Mina.'

I stared at a young girl sitting at the peat fire, a mug of tea in one hand and a scone and jam in the other. 'Hallo, Craig,' she said.

'What the hell are you doing here?'

'Thanks for the welcome, big brother.'

I walked over to where she was sitting. 'You're Jean,' I said, holding out my hand. She took it in hers and smiled.

'Right first time. My, you have turned out a good looker. You will stand out, head and shoulders above everybody at the wedding. Won't she, Craig?'

'How did you get out here? When did you come and who brought you?' Craig demanded, all in one breath.

'What are all the questions for? You would think I'd committed a crime. I live here with my mother when I'm not in school, remember?'

'Answer my questions, Jean, and less cheek.'

Jean tossed her head. 'Well, question one, Donald brought me. Oh, a message from Donald, Mina. He is sorry he couldn't wait to see you tonight. He had to get back to Drumoich, but is coming tomorrow.' She looked back at her brother. 'Question two, I arrived at eight o'clock. You and Mina had just gone, Mum said, and question three, I got here by car—Donald's.'

I was looking at Craig who was looking down at his sister. I had a good idea what he was thinking. I wanted to laugh at the trick fate had played on us, but Craig certainly wasn't laughing. 'Go to bed, Jean,' Craig said at last.

'Oh Craig, now? I haven't even got speaking to Mina yet and, anyway, I'm sixteen.'

'You can talk to Mina tomorrow. Go to bed.'

She rose reluctantly. 'Are you coming, Mina, and we can talk in bed?'

'Mina isn't going up yet. We want to talk,' Craig replied.

'Goodnight then, Mina. I bet you're glad you didn't marry him after all. He's an old crab.' She went out and shut the door. Craig sat down in the chair opposite me and pulled the stool over from behind his chair. 'Sit here, Mina, beside me.' I sat down beside him. 'I wonder, what is Donald's game?' he said.

I didn't want to discuss Donald. I knew his game. His mother must have mentioned Craig was staying the night at the Brae House. I put my arms around Craig's neck. 'Never mind Craig, no one can separate us,' I said softly. We rose, Craig blew out the lamp, and hand in hand, we ascended the stair I knew so well. We kissed goodnight and went to our separate rooms.

Chapter 31

Next morning I was up early, but Craig had gone.

At ten o'clock I presented myself at Mary's. My dress was tried on, taken off, pinned up and tried on again. To my surprise, Nan was an excellent tailoress and certainly knew her job. Mrs McAndrew threw instructions and counter instructions about all day. Wedding presents were being unpacked, letters of thanks were being written, and a constant stream of people, mostly women, came and went. It was three in the afternoon when Jean came in.

'Mina,' she said, sticking her head round the parlour door where Nan was putting the finishing touches to my dress. 'I am going to Drumoich on my bike. Is there a message or anything?'

'Yes, Jean, there is. Just a moment.' I went to the door and as I passed, drew it gently behind me. 'Will you ask John to come to the Brae House tonight. I haven't met his wife.' I knew if John and his wife came, Donald wouldn't come. I would need to stay in the house and entertain them, which wouldn't suit Donald at all and Craig was coming on Thursday. I realized I wasn't deceiving the sharp Jean very much, but she said she would do as I asked.

It was eight o'clock that night when, with all of us exhausted, Mrs McAndrew called for a halt.

'Come out this way, Mina,' Mary indicated the front door,

and once outside, drew it behind her. 'Was Craig here last night?'

I nodded. 'Yes, he was. How did you know?'

'It was Peter who saw his car sitting at the end of the Brae House,' she explained. 'Nan said it was there all night and left this morning at six-thirty. She heard it leave.'

I faced Mary. 'If Nan would only mind her own business.'

'Stop, Mina,' Mary broke in, 'Nan knows nothing about you and Craig. She just thought he was there visiting his mother. But I know. Mum told me all about it when I was on holiday two years ago. Your name cropped up and it all came out. The whole reason I brought the subject up was to say I could never have done what you did, sacrificing your happiness in order to benefit the one you cared for. I just couldn't have done it.'

'Yes you could, Mary, if you loved enough. Goodnight.'

Chapter 32

Next day was the show of presents which went on all day and until nine o'clock that night. My voice was hoarse repeating the same things over and over again and telling the stream of visitors who sent what. There were two or three hundred presents on show. Only a hundred guests were invited to the church, but over two hundred would be coming to the reception in the barn. This was a Highland wedding. No one was left out, man, woman or child.

It was nearly nine o'clock when I arrived back at the Brae House, and as I was about to open the door, it was opened for me by Craig. We embraced on the doorstep. 'Oh Craig, I'm so tired,' I yawned.

He nodded. 'Jean,' he called into the kitchen, 'I'm taking Mina up to her bed. Tell Mum when she comes.' Then he lifted me up as if I were a child, carried me upstairs to my room and laid me gently down on the bed. 'I'll let you rest,' he said. 'See you tomorrow.'

'Not tomorrow, Craig,' I said, 'I'm sleeping with Mary tomorrow night. Mark Dewar and his parents are coming from Rothesay and staying here. I've no idea where everybody else from Rothesay is going to sleep, but I've no doubt Mrs McAndrew has everything under control.'

'Then I won't see you until the wedding,' he said.

I shook my head. 'It seems not, Craig.'

'It doesn't matter,' he said cheerfully. 'You are not going back to Aberdeen anyway. I told mother tonight that you are staying here—for good.'

I sat up. 'Craig. Listen to me.'

'Look, Mina, I listened to you four years ago, and lost you. You're not going back.' He bent down and kissed me tenderly on the check. 'Goodnight, sweetheart.'

After he went downstairs, I undressed and got into bed, so tired that I couldn't think straight. I am not going back . . . I am staying in the Glen . . . I am going back . . . and with these thoughts buzzing in my brain, finally fell asleep.

Friday was a much quieter day. Visitors were met off the bus at Dalreigh brought up to Balgreig, introduced and shown where they were to spend the weekend. I liked Mark Dewar and his brother Bill, who was to be best man. Their parents and relations were down to earth with the hail-fellow-well-met attitudes that one finds anywhere in the West of Scotland. They seemed to work hard and play hard, and I liked them very much. Some belonged to Glasgow, Clydebank, The Gareloch, Dunoon and Rothesay. Mary was going to be a lucky lassie with so many relations and friends.

Her wedding day arrived, the weather held and it was going to be a glorious day. We rose, dressed and went downstairs at eight o'clock. Nan, Peter and their father were the only ones up before us.

We ate breakfast and had just risen from the table when Mary making for the door, turned to me, saying 'Mina, leave the dishes and come on.'

'Where are you going?' asked Nan.

'Riding,' said Mary.

'You can't go riding on your wedding day,' said Nan angrily. 'Dad, do something, don't just stand there and let these two idiots go riding.'

'Now, Nan,' he said, smiling at Mary. 'It's only nine o'clock in the morning and the wedding isn't until three in the afternoon. What harm is there?'

'I'm going to see my mother.' Nan made for the door leading to the foot of the stairs.

'You will leave your mother where she is.' Andrew's voice had the ring of authority. 'Go on, the pair of you,' he said kindly. 'The horses are in the paddock behind the Brae House.' He turned to Peter. 'Go and get them lad and saddle them up. I don't suppose you two will be wanting to ride bare-back now. Anyway those horses are more accustomed to the saddle.'

We followed Peter, and the horses were soon saddled. They weren't heavy horses, mostly used for the trap to take the family to church and other places.

'You ride Prince, Mina,' Mary instructed, pointing to a black horse with a white star on his forehead. 'I'll take Duke,' and drew him to a large boulder at the stable door which we had always used when we mounted Bute and Jess. I hadn't ridden since I had left school, and Prince looked very big.

'Not afraid, are you, Mina?' said a deep voice from the barn door.

I was standing on the large boulder. 'Craig.' I gave a cry of delight. 'Where have you come from?'

'I arrived from Drumoich this morning. The Brae House is packed with visitors so I came to see if I could find you.' He stood beside me. 'Want me to give you a leg up?' he asked mischievously.

'No thank you,' I replied in the same bantering tone. 'I haven't forgotten how to mount a horse.'

Mary had already mounted and was sitting watching us. Peter at the stable door was also watching us. I mounted. Craig held the bridle for a moment and said, 'Have a nice ride. See you in church.' His voice was a caress in itself.

I nodded happily and joined Mary. The horses moved away at walking pace. We were passing the Brae House when a small, fair-haired person came out of the house. I thought she was one of the Rothesay crowd, and yet I hadn't remembered seeing her before. She was staring at me and I smiled down at her. Mary drew her horse beside mine as we passed the gate. 'That's Craig's wife, Mina.'

I felt no emotion, neither jealousy nor guilt. 'Oh is it?' I said. 'I'll likely be introduced later on.' Then I forgot her.

The horses started to trot and I was beginning to enjoy myself. Horse riding is like everything else. Once a rider, always a rider. When we arrived at the Lochan, the horses were still trotting. 'Let's gallop them, Mina,' Mary called from behind.

'Yes, let's,' I said, 'and when we come to the gate at the moor, let's not stop to open it, let's leap the fence.'

'That means we will have to leap the ditch at the same time,' she called back.

'That's right, let's go,' I shouted, and hitting Prince's flanks with my stirrups, we were off. I felt exhilarated. The fresh morning air blew on our faces, our hair gleamed in the morning sun, horse and rider were as one. I could have gone on like this forever. The horses were still at full gallop when the moor came into view. We were nearing the fence. I had full control of the bridle and the horse's head. 'Come on Prince,' I urged,' I know you can do it.' We were up and over.

It wasn't until we drew the horses up and dismounted, that we realised what a dangerous jump we had taken. 'I don't think we could have done that bareback,' I said, eyeing the gate.

'I doubt it,' she laughed. 'Mina, let's make a pact. Let's come up to the Glen at the same time every year.' At that moment we felt happy, carefree and young and the world was our oyster, and I agreed heartily.

We were still in this mood when we returned. Mrs McAndrew was outside waiting for us and as we dismounted, she called to Peter to take the horses. 'Do you two know the time, it's nearly twelve o'clock. Mary, just look at you and on your wedding day too. You are a mess. And so are you.' She turned an angry face towards me. 'Get into the house, both of you.' We both giggled as we went upstairs to tidy ourselves before going down to lunch.

Before we realised it, it was time to dress the bride in her long dress of white figured satin. Her tiara was of white rosebuds holding her veil, which was waist length. Her bouquet was pink and red roses, mingled with green fern. 'I think you are the most beautiful bride I'll ever see, Mary,' I said smiling.

Her mother, trying to hide her emotion, chipped in 'That's a compliment indeed for you, dear, and from another woman too.'

Mary turned to her. 'Thanks for everything, Mum,' and gave her mother's wet cheek a kiss.

My dress was pink, long like Mary's, and when I swung round, it billowed all about me. There was no shortage of material there. On my head was a garland of pink roses, pinned there by Nan. My bouquet was like Mary's only slightly smaller. The taxis arrived from MacBrayne's Garage in Inverness. Nan called up to her mother, 'Come on, Mum.'

I was going in the same taxi as Mary and her father and five minutes later it arrived. Mary and her father sat in the back and I was in front with the driver. In fifteen minutes, we had arrived at the Wee Free Church, where I got out and Mary and her father followed.

'You look well in the kilt,' I said to Mr McAndrew. I had to say something, and could see he was upset. He was after all, handing over his youngest daughter to a man we scarcely knew who was taking her away to Rothesay—a place where Mr McAndrew had never been.

We started to walk down the aisle, Mary on her father's arm and me bringing up the rear. Mark and his brother were already in their places. As Mary approached, Mark turned and smiled at his bride. I saw him take her hand and squeeze it. The minister was about to start the ceremony. 'Who giveth this woman in marriage.?'

'I do,' Mr McAndrew said, and stepped back. The service had started. I took Mary's bouquet from her while Mark put the gold band on her finger. The ceremony came to an end. They were man and wife. After the signing of the register, Mary and Mark went back down the aisle together, with Bill and me following. Two pipers were playing when we got outside the church. Cameras started to click. Everyone came out of the church and started making for the horse-drawn traps, motor-bikes, push bikes and the few private cars. It was going to be a big job getting everyone back to the barn at Balgreig, but an hour later, we were all there.

Mary and Mark, Bill and I waited indoors in her mother's house until we got the signal that the reception was about to begin. We emerged to a battery of cameras again, the skirl of the pipes and to a crowd of about two hundred people. It was certainly the gathering of the clans and every man wore the kilt belonging to his. The guests lined up outside the barn, making a passageway for the bride and groom. There was no need for handshaking and anyway it would have taken too long. We followed the pipers in and right up to the top table. When we were all seated, the pipes ceased.

The bride and groom rose and cut the cake to rapturous applause. The minister said grace. The feast had begun. We were served by a catering firm from Inverness. Whisky glasses were filled for the men, as the toasts were about to begin, Bill, the best man, rose raising his glass. 'To the bride and groom,' The company stood, faced the happy couple; 'Slainte,' and drained their glasses. After the speeches, congratulations and telegrams were given and read, and the tables were cleared and removed. Bales of hay were put against the walls for seats and chairs were only for the elderly. The band, consisting of two fiddles, an accordion and a piano, was at the end of the bar, which with dozens of bottles of whisky, was at the other end.

The bride and groom were the first to take the floor, followed by Bill and myself, and then everyone joined in. After the first dance, I was standing talking to Bill when a hand touched my shoulder. It was Craig. 'It's a military-two step, Mina.' I slipped into his arms. 'You are very beautiful,' he whispered.

I laughed happily. 'You look very, very handsome in your

kilt, Craig. You fairly suit it and I'm awfully proud of you.' He smiled into my eyes.

'I won't see much of you until the bride and groom leave.' The dance finished. 'Would you like to meet Liz?' he asked. 'You don't have to if you don't want to.'

'I don't mind, Craig.' We approached a young girl sitting beside Craig's mother, whom I had seen at the Brae House that morning. She was small and fair, but this time I noticed her eyes, which were the blue of a china doll. Craig introduced us. She held out her hand, but barely touched mine. I couldn't, by any stretch of the imagination, think of her as Craig's wife. Her voice was pleasant enough as she said, 'Craig has told me all about you, Mina.'

Someone came over to speak to Craig, so his back was turned from us for a few minutes. Liz took me by surprise a moment later when she said, 'I understand what you two mean to each other, but there is nothing, no nothing, I will do to make it easier for you to get him.'

Anger rose inside me, then died. 'Liz,' I said, and the words were out before I could stop them, 'it doesn't matter what you do now or any other time, because some day, one day, Craig and I will be together. We can wait, even if it's for a lifetime.' My voice died away and I turned towards Craig. Liz was forgotten.

The dance and all that followed was a grand affair. Gaelic songs were sung with gusto and, at other times, with tender emotion, as only the Highlander can sing. There were recitations, some comical, some serious, but all thoroughly enjoyable. The set dances were danced in perfect rhythm to the pipes or fiddles. When Old Jock, the piper—I never knew his second name—and his son, Archie felt dry, the music was passed on to the fiddlers, and vice versa. There was no let up. The whisky flowed from the bottles like water from a stream. There was no beer, only whisky. To have had any other kind of drink at a Highland wedding in those days, was considered an insult to the guests.

At ten o'clock, a taxi arrived to take the bride and groom to an Inverness hotel for the night and what a send off they got! It was a good job Mary hadn't her wedding dress on. She had changed into her going-away clothes and I into a dance dress.

At one side of the hall the male guests gathered around Mark and on the opposite side, the female guests surrounded Mary. Two blankets appeared from nowhere and Mary and Mark were tossed into the air about half a dozen times, then carried over the heads of the crowd to the door. I had Mary's handbag and gloves but couldn't get near her. Some of the guests saw my plight and lifted me bodily above the crowd until I reached the taxi. Then the rice started. What missed Mark and Mary, hit me, full on the face and for anyone who hasn't had this experience, believe me, it's very painful. Confetti was never used up there at that time, at least not at Mary's wedding. I handed Mary her gloves and handbag. 'Good luck, Mary, goodbye,' and the taxi door slammed shut and they were off. My duties as a bridesmaid were finished.

I was the last to enter the barn and above the din and laughter I could hear Old Jock playing *The Hills of Home* on his pipes. That heart-rending tune always brings a lump to my throat. I just stood where I was until the last note died away into silence. When I entered the barn, the lanterns were being lit and placed in strategic points around the barn. They were quite safe really, each lamp having a kind of wire surrounding it. The older people were making tracks for home and the barn and the dance was left to the younger ones. Tomorrow was the Sabbath and the dance would finish just before midnight.

The fiddlers called out, 'Eightsome Reel. Gentlemen, take your partners.' Craig was at my side. I don't know where he came from, he was just there, but it was enough for me and he took my hand and led me on to the floor. 'You are not a bridemaid now, Mina, you are mine again. I've been waiting for this moment.'

'So have I, Craig.' We finished the dance and were still holding hands when a slow waltz was announced. We just drifted onto the floor again. I could feel the warmth of Craig's body as he pressed it to mine. He buried his face in my hair and whispered in my ear. 'Let's get out of here.'

'Yes, Craig,' I whispered back, completely unaware of anything or anyone.

We were dancing towards the door when someone spoke behind me. 'Hallo, Mina. Do you know I haven't seen you since you came back.'

It was Alex, Craig's brother, holding out his hand. I held out mine as if in a dream. In Craig's arms I had forgotten where I was. 'For God's sake, Craig.' Alex was speaking in a slow deliberate voice. 'What do you think you are playing at?'

I realised then that Alex hadn't come to speak to me by accident. He must have been watching us. 'I know you don't care a damn for Liz, but you do care for all these people in here, and so do you, Mina.'

'Look, Alex, all these people here know all about us,' Craig said quietly, 'and you are not going to tell me differently.'

Alex, ignoring his brother, turned to me. 'Craig has a job to do at Northfield, Mina. Since he married Liz, we have the money to carry on.'

Northfield again. 'Alex,' my voice was shaking with anger, 'I will never take Craig from Northfield, but what Craig and I do together, is not your business. Now, if you will excuse us, we would like to dance.'

I was thankful that Craig was distracted by his sister Jean during this exchange, and hadn't heard Alex's remark to me. The men had had a lot to drink and I wanted no trouble. 'But you haven't danced with me, Craig,' Jean was saying. 'Come on, it's the Gay Gordons, tell him to give me this dance, Mina.'

I laughed, all anger gone. 'I think you can manage that yourself, without any assistance,' I said kindly.

Now Peter McAndrew touched my arm. 'Dancing, Mina?' and with a sigh of relief I took the floor with Peter. It was nearing midnight. Old Jock was out for the count, and while the fiddlers were still on their feet, the accordianist and pianist were gone. Bill, Mark's brother, announced the last dance and then came over to me. 'What a wonderful wedding it has been,' he said, as we danced.

After the first part of the last dance was finished, the parents of the bride and groom were placed in the centre of the floor. We all sang *For they are Jolly Good Fellows* and the wedding finished with *Auld Lang Syne*.

Outside, rows of horses and traps waited for the guests, supervised by Peter and his father. Craig's car drew up beside me. Liz was sitting beside him with Alex and Jean in the back. I looked at her, Craig's wife. She seemed so small sitting beside him, and I felt terribly sorry for her. Her money was being poured into Northfield and what was she getting in return? Certainly not Craig. And Alex and Craig would see that she didn't get Northfield either. On impulse I held out my hand to her. Before taking it, she drew off her gloves.

'Goodbye, I'm glad I've met you,' she said.

'So am I. Goodbye.' I was never to see Elizabeth Leitch again.

I slept with Mrs McKenzie that night in Uncle Dunk's room. Mrs McAndrew needed Mary's room for friends who wanted to stay.

Chapter 33

Sunday morning was another lovely day and I was up early. Everyone was preparing to go to church after breakfast, but I stayed behind.

Silence enveloped the Brae House when they had gone. I went to sit beside Uncle Dunk's place beside the peat fire, gazing around the kitchen where I had been brought up. Then I went into the small bedroom, knelt down beside the bed with my head on my hands. How long I knelt there I don't know, but something strange and unnatural was entering this little room. It seemed as if Uncle Dunk was lying on the bed. I could feel his presence so strongly that I started to speak aloud.

'Uncle Dunk, what am I to do? Stay here with Craig, or go back?'

'Go back, Mina,' a loving, well-known voice seemed to say. 'You and Craig will come together one day, but not yet.'

I was terrified. I dropped my hands from my face and stared at the bed, but there was no one there. I rose from my knees, hardly able to control my fear, then the turmoil inside me stilled.

I left the Brae House and made for the hills. The Highlands were entering the breathtaking splendour of Autumn. I knew I wouldn't see my friends, the great stag, nor the deer, they would still be well up the mountain. But I did see the Golden Eagle. I had reached the summit of the hill, and the view from the other side of Tomnaloich was as beautiful as the picture imprinted in my mind. It was beautiful, but more savage. Range upon range of mountains met my gaze. A small river gurgled over rocks and stones hundreds of feet below in one of the gorges between the mountains. The only sign of life was the birch and hazel trees, and even they didn't grow very far up the mountain.

It was then I saw the eagle. The eagle, like the deer, kept well away in summer. It had risen from the gorge, or was it one of the trees? I couldn't make out because I was too far away, but it hovered for a few minutes high above the place where I saw it rise. No wonder it was called the King of Birds. It was majestically beautiful, it's plummage like burnished gold against the sun. It soared up the mountain and away, probably to it's eyrie high on a mountain cliff. This was in the days before the tourists flocked to the Glen. What a lot the people of the Lowlands missed, I thought, never to see such sights as I was feasting my eyes on now.

I sat on a large boulder, letting my thoughts wander, and thinking that if all the great leaders of the world could come here on a summer day to discuss their differences and drink in the glory spread out before them, the world would be a far better place.

After a while, reluctantly, I rose and started down the hill. When I came to the Lochan I picked up some small flat stones and idly skimmed them over the still, sparkling waters, as Mary and I had done as children.

Then, suddenly, I felt a presence behind me and turned. It was Craig, standing on a small hillock, his two hands in his pockets, legs astride. He had a white polo-necked jersey on over brown trousers and his handsome face was crowned with thick, slightly curly, dark hair. He always reminded me of an athlete. I looked at him and went on looking, standing there, the love in my eyes reflected in his. As he approached, he drew me to him and kissed me.

'I have been watching you, Mina, ever since you left the top of the hill. You came from the other side, I noticed. Why did you go there, since there is nothing there but mountains?'

'There is everything there, Craig,' I said quietly. I took his hand. 'I didn't mean to be so late. We'd better get back.' We walked in silence. I didn't wish to break the harmony between us by saying that I was going.

'I don't like you going so far up the hill, Mina, especially over the other side.' Craig's eyes took on a worried look. 'It's all right in summer, I admit, but you will be here in the winter too and you know these mountains as well as I do, how in a matter of minutes the mist comes down. I hope you will never attempt the hill during a time of snow. I just don't understand this love you have for the mountains and the mad attraction for water. It worries me.' Craig drew me close and sighed. 'Mina, I have an awful feeling, deep inside, that I am losing you again.'

We were back to four years ago and I had to tell Craig I was leaving. Alex was right to stop us last night. He knew what we were about to do and, like us, he also knew that if we did what was in our minds, there would be no turning back.

'You are running away from me again,' Craig was saying. 'You can't run all your life, Mina, take a stand now and stay where you belong.'

'Craig, it would be Heaven for me to do as you ask. You said once that the Glen was your rival. Well, the Black Isle is mine, and Northfield, thanks to your Uncle and Liz's father. At least you have seen what you consider your rival,' I said with a sweep of my arm. 'I have never seen mine. I have never even been there.'

'Stay with me and you will be there, tonight, tomorrow, any time you like.'

I stared at Craig's handsome face. He means it, I thought, he really means it. He would actually take me to Northfield, and Liz and Alex would be ousted as of no importance, and I, for one awful moment, was a willing partner. I wanted desperately to go and to hang with the consequences, and be with him always. But something inside kept repeating, don't go, Mina, don't do it. We had been holding each other, but now I drew back slowly. 'I am returning South tomorrow. Go back to Northfield tonight, please, Craig.'

His face was white and his eyes black with anger, but slowly, his face cleared and the anger left his eyes. He took my hand and in a resigned voice said, 'You must be hungry, Mina, I know I am. Let's go to the Brae House.'

Mrs McKenzie was sitting reading the Bible when we entered. 'Where on earth have you been, Mina? Where did you find her, Craig? The visitors were looking for you to say goodbye and Mrs McAndrew is very angry. Why did you have to go running away like that?' Meg said, in her soft Gaelic voice.

'I wasn't running away, I just wanted to go up the hill.' I looked at the peat fire. To keep food hot, the dishes were put on top of hot bricks. It didn't take any of the flavour away, as long as the dishes were covered over. I was starving and enjoyed my combined dinner and tea very much, for it was nearly five. There was no need to wash the dishes as this was the Sabbath, so I piled them up beside the rest on the kist. Meg went back to reading the Good Book, as the Bible was usually called, and I was sitting aimlessly opposite her. Craig was pacing about from the fire to the door, from the door to the window and back to the fire. His mother stopped her reading, took off her glasses and watched him. She looked at me and then back to Craig. I could see she was very concerned. To ease the situation I blurted out, 'I'm going down to Aberdeen tomorrow. I start work on Tuesday.'

Mrs McKenzie didn't answer me. 'Craig,' she said, 'It's time you were going, you have a long road in front of you, to the Black Isle.'

He turned to where his mother was sitting. 'I'm going tomorrow.' Mother and son faced each other. 'You heard what Mina said. She goes tomorrow, and you go tonight.'

Funny, I thought, it was four years ago in this very house that

Craig and I were torn apart. 'Craig,' I rose and put my hand on his arm. 'Mary and I made a pact yesterday, that every year at this time, we would come back to the Glen.'

'So, it's to be an annual meeting and parting,' said Craig sarcastically.

'Sit down, boy,' his mother spoke quietly and gently, 'and let's see things right.' He drew a chair over and sat beside me. I took his hand in mine, waiting for his mother to speak. Meg looked at Craig. 'When you married Liz you took vows . . .'

'In a Registry Office. It meant nothing to me,' interrupted Craig.

'Nevertheless,' continued his mother, ignoring him, 'she has ploughed her share of the money into Northfield. You are going to benefit and you are going to have a grand place there some-day. So go back to Northfield, Craig, and give Liz back some-thing in place of what she has given you. She deserves peace and respect from you. See that she gets it, Craig.' Meg looked at me, then at Craig. 'Mina has given up a great deal so that you could farm Northfield, with the help of Liz's money. Do you think it was an easy decision for her. I knew it wasn't. I knew it the moment she came in here on Tuesday night.' She took a deep breath. 'Now I'm speaking to both of you. I don't, in any way understand this love you both have for each other, and I am sure few people can, but it's not good, not good at all, at all. It's hurting too many people.' She rose with a sigh. 'Now, I'm going to the McAndrews for Jean. I asked her to stay there until I had talked to you both. When I come back, lad, I want you to be on your way to the Black Isle.' She wrapped her shawl around her shoulders and was gone.

Craig raised his head. 'Why can't we have more than one wife, as they have in India and other countries?'

I smiled at him. 'It's just the system, Craig, and you can't beat it, I learned that a long time ago.'

He rose and drew me into his embrace, and gently brushed my cheek up and down with his own. 'So it's back to North-field . . .' His voice broke. I was glad we weren't looking at each other for my eyes were filled with tears. 'But I will tell you this, Mina,' he swallowed hard, 'we will be together some day, I promise you that.'

'Yes Craig, I know we will, I know.' He was trembling, then he slackened his hold and a moment later I heard the door close.

Chapter 34

On Tuesday morning I presented myself back at the Hotel for
duty. No wonder I was considered a good worker. It was only
with hard work and no let-up that I was able to carry on, and to
try to forget. Then Bill Southall came up to Aberdeen a fortnight after my return. Poor Bill, it wasn't my weekend off, and I
made work the excuse for not seeing much of him and it was the
third week of September when my weekend-off came round
before with Bill's insistence, I promised to go to The Mains.
When I did he met me at Pirnhill Station, his face glowing with
happiness. His mother and brother Angus were pleased to see
me too, and made me very welcome. Rita, her husband, Edith
and Bob were invited up along with other friends I had made in
Turlum village so we had quite a party.

On Sunday, Bill took me round some of the lovely spots he
knew I would like. Perthshire is a beautiful county with some
wonderful scenery and I liked it very much. He knew this, and
as we were walking said to me, 'This could be your home, you
know.'

'I'm not ready for a home,' I replied. I was putting him off,
for I knew what was to come.

'Let's get engaged, Mina.'

'No, Bill.' The words came out in so startled a fashion that he
looked at me in surprise.

'Let's sit here,' he said, indicating a fallen tree trunk at the
side of the path. 'Mina, do you mind if I ask you something?'

'Of course not, Bill.' I wasn't looking at him but arranging
my skirt after sitting down.

'Is there someone else?' I looked at him now. His fine eyes
were watching me intently. 'Just tell me the truth, Mina. I'll
understand and I won't be hurt.'

But he would be hurt and I didn't want to hurt Bill. How
could I tell him about Craig, how could I explain this love that
was inside me? Bill's love was quiet, gentle, undemanding. Why
not, I asked myself, marry this kind man. What have you to lose?

'Tell you what, Bill,' I said, without answering his question.
'If you are still of the same mind on my birthday, we will get
engaged.'

He drew me gently into his arms and forgot his question, for
the time being anyway. He kissed me on the lips. 'When is
your birthday?'

'June, next year.'

'Oh, that's not fair. That's nine months away.'

'But we will see each other,' I compromised. 'You will be up in Aberdeen and I'll come to The Mains.' Bill had to be content with that.

The weeks passed quickly—all too quickly—and before I realised it, we were entertaining the Festive Season, and the Festive Season is a very busy time in a Hotel. Some nights, I went home on the last tram to Aunt Kate's, exhausted. After the Festive Season, there was a lull, and the winter dragged on to spring. My annual holiday was due.

When Mr Withers came to tell me to go on holiday from the 7th April until the 21st, my mind flew instantly to the Glen. Most of the mountains would still be shrouded in snow, the heather would be green. If I was there now, I would probably hear, standing at the Brae House door, all the small birds, singing and chirping their little hearts out, especially in early morning and just before dark. The ice would be melting on the Lochan. How I longed to go there! But instead, I went for a week to The Mains and most of the second week I spent down at the beach. At night, I danced in the Beach Ballroom, a favourite haunt of the hotel workers. June came in, as June does often with a blaze of sunshine. Bill was coming up on the Saturday nearest my birthday. We were to buy the ring.

Aunt Kate said it called for a celebration. 'No Aunt Kate,' I said firmly, 'we will just go somewhere quiet for a meal.' But I reckoned without the staff.

A lot of them had met Bill when he called for me at the hotel. All the stillroom maids knew him, a lot of the chambermaids too and, of course, the waiters and kitchen staff. They all liked him.

When he arrived off the train, he called for me at the hotel and then we went out to buy the ring. I had promised I would take Bill back to the staffroom to let them see my ring. The amount of staff that were off duty that day certainly surprised me. We were given a slap-up meal and handed lots of presents for my bottom drawer, as they said. I was very moved. I wonder what they would have said, that grand lot of friends, if they knew what I was really like. I wanted to shout at them, 'You fools, can't you see I don't want your friendship, nor your presents. This ring means nothing. The man I love isn't Bill, it's someone else.' But I knew I would never say words like that. I wouldn't dream of going against the System. It wouldn't be right, it wouldn't be proper. The System must be upheld at all costs.

At the end of July, I received a letter from Jean, and in a small paragraph were the words; 'Craig's wife had a baby boy last week.' I was pleased. I knew for his son's sake, Craig would never leave Northfield now, but what I was surprised at was that his son was born at Drumoich. Jean had just stated the facts. 'Tell you more about it when I write again,' she wrote. I would probably hear more about it when I went up in August.

But I didn't go up in August. I received a letter from Mary, who hadn't been too well and was in hospital, so we would have to cancel our pact this year.

My life in Aberdeen, although busy and quiet, was happy enough. My thoughts of the Glen were both turmoil and ecstasy, with the craving for Craig always with me, but here it was bearable, while up there, in the Glen beside him, it knew no bounds. My love for the Glen was also kept well in check down here, although terrible homesickness overwhelmed me at times. But there was also Bill, gentle, warm-hearted Bill, the man I couldn't hurt. So time passed pleasantly enough.

Bill wanted me to name the day of our wedding when I was down at The Mains just before Christmas, but again, I put him off. 'If I get rooms in the village,' he said, 'will you name the day then?' I nodded absently. It wasn't so easy to get a house, so it didn't trouble me very much then, but I knew it was just as matter of time before, with the help of Edith and Rita, he got a home for me. Edith was married now and living in the village not far from Rita. I had been unable to get to her wedding as it took place during Hogmanay, when it was impossible to get away from the hotel.

It was now January, 1939.

When Bill arrived up at Aunt Kate's one Saturday, he had news for me. He had found a house. Rita's mother-in-law was moving into a smaller house, so instead of selling her old home, she was letting it to Bill. 'There is nothing to stop us now, except for you to name the day, Mina,' he said softly.

Aunt Kate and Uncle Willie were delighted. 'I will give you your wedding, Mina,' Aunt Kate said, 'you don't have to worry about a thing.' I didn't want a big wedding, but she wouldn't listen. And Bill? One night he took me in his arms and I pushed him away, saying 'I can't marry you, Bill, I just can't.'

'What's the matter with you? I just don't understand.'

When I remained silent, he just stood there, gazing at me. 'Look, Mina, I know you are not madly in love with me, but that will come with time. I've known lots of people who only liked and respected each other, then when they got married, the rest followed automatically. And I love you, very, very much. So, we are half way there.' Still I remained silent. 'Mina, I asked you this question before, is there someone else? If there is, I would like to know.'

A voice inside me kept repeating, tell him, tell him. But I couldn't. I raised my eyes from the floor and I saw the love in his eyes, on his face, and I couldn't. I just couldn't. How could I tell a man like Bill of the wild love—as Craig's mother had put it—between Craig and myself, of how we were torn apart twice in four years by convention, and how in tearing us apart, convention had only made our love more passionate and lasting. Bill was a down-to-earth chap. He could never understand a love like that, so I just shook my head and buried my face in his coat. He held me against him. 'We will be happy, you'll see. I will be good to you, Mina.' I had no doubts whatever about that.

The wedding was finally fixed for the third week in April. I wrote to Jean, Craig's sister and told her. I also wrote to Mary in Rothesay. They would get their invitations in due course, but they were such dear friends that I wanted to tell them myself, personally. Time seemed to fly past. The invitations were out and some acceptances had already come back. My dress was bought. It was the first week of April.

My two cousins were to be my bridesmaids. I had to see the minister, Mr Marshall, so Aunt Kate came with me, as he was her minister and she was a churchgoer, although I wasn't. Mr Marshall wanted my Birth Certificate.

'That will be quite easy to supply,' said Aunt Kate. 'I have it.' Later that evening, Aunt Kate rummaged through drawers and cupboards. 'That's funny, I was sure I had your Birth Certificate, Mina. Never mind, I'll get it sometime this week. at the Registrar's.' But next day, Wednesday, I was off duty, and it was Vera's half day, so we arranged to meet at one-thirty so that she could help me choose my wedding shoes.

On our way, we had to pass the Registry Office and she mentioned my birth certificate. 'Come on in here, Mina, We will get your Birth Certificate. It will save Mum. You know what she's like, when she comes in for her shopping—always laden.' Actually, I had forgotten all about the certificate.

We entered the building that Mrs Armstrong and I had been in once before, and made our way to the Registrar's upstairs. A woman came forward and asked our requirements. Vera gave me a nudge. 'Go on Mina, ask her.'

'I would like my birth certificate, please.'

'Give me your full name and date of birth.'

I did this. She disappeared and, in about ten minutes returned and handed me a folded sheet of paper. 'That will be three shillings, please.' I dished out the money and took the certificate.

We were down at the bottom of the stairs when I stopped and opened up the certificate out of curiosity. Vera kept walking on. 'Vera,' I called, 'come back, this is not mine, there has been a mistake. Let's go back.'

My cousin, took the certificate out of my hand and read it. She studied it for a minute or two. 'Well,' she said, puzzled. 'It has the same name as yours and same date of birth, but according to this, there is no father's name. Whoever this is, she is illegitimate. What a shame.'

I took the piece of paper from her. 'I'm taking it back.'

We returned, and it was the same woman who approached us. I handed her the certificate. 'This is not mine. My parents were married.' She took the paper out of my hand and looked at me, then disappeared. This time she was away much longer and on returning she was not alone. An elderly gentleman was with her. It was Mr Wilson. He smiled. 'Hallo.'

He was holding the paper in his hand. 'This,' he said quietly, 'is yours.' He handed the paper back to me. I just stared at it, it was Vera who took it.

'I'm sorry my dear, but did you not know? You should have been told.'

'I don't want your sympathy. That's not mine,' I argued.

Just then, Vera gave an 'Oohh,' of astonishment. 'Do you see who your mother is?' she gasped. 'It's Aunt Ann! Honest it is, Mina. Look.' She was shoving the piece of paper into my face.

'Give that back, Vera, it's not mine,' I said obstinately.

Mr Wilson looked at me with compassion. That look was enough. I knew the certificate Vera was gasping at was mine, I didn't have to look at Mr Wilson. In silence, Vera handed me the paper. She was realising that this was no joke.

We were outside standing on the pavement. Carefully I put the piece of paper into my handbag while Vera watched me closely. We started to walk towards George Street to get a tram for home. 'Do you see who your mother is?' Vera asked again. I didn't answer. 'It's Aunt Ann. Fancy Aunt Ann having a baby twenty five years ago.' She started to giggle again. 'Wonder who the father was, or is?' She rambled on.

The tram arrived. We entered and took a seat. Vera paid the fares, but I just sat. When we arrived home I had not uttered a word. The rage, humiliation and hurt pride inside me can never be described.

Aunt Kate knew the moment she saw me that something was wrong. 'What's the matter?' she asked anxiously. I removed my coat and hung it up carefully in the lobby, then removed my scarf and hung that up too, picked my handbag up off the floor, entered the sitting room, sat down and opened my handbag. Everything I did was slow and deliberate.

Vera hadn't spoken since we entered. I think she was afraid, but unable to control herself any longer, her words came out now with a rush. 'Mum, Aunt Ann has had a baby, and it's Mina.'

I produced the certificate from my bag. 'How . . . ? Who . . . ?' Aunt Kate got no further. So she knows, I thought, and has known all the time. I rose, threw the certificate at her. 'Read it,' I shouted, 'read it, both of you.'

Uncle Willie got to his feet. 'Now Mina,' he soothed.

'Liars, hypocrites, all of you,' I kept shouting. 'Why didn't you tell me? Why didn't you? Was it to save *her* face?' I heard the door open and I turned. Aunt Ann—my mother—was standing with Eva, who must have just come in. I knew by her face that she had heard me.

'Compose yourself, lassie, and sit down.' It was Uncle Willie speaking.

'Look, Mina,' Aunt Kate said. 'What was the point of telling you. If you hadn't gone for your birth certificate, it's a question if you would ever have found out, and your Aunt Ann has a large circle of friends who know nothing about you.'

'It must have been very heart searching,' I said sarcastically, 'when I came into your lives, to explain me to all your friends. I will enjoy listening to the lies you must have told them.'

'That will do, Mina,' Uncle Willie said sternly.

'And you,' I said, ignoring Uncle Willie and turning to Aunt Ann who was standing silently near the door. 'You are the worst of all. I was your child, your flesh and blood, yet you deserted me, threw me to the Authorities. I was left to be brought up by the parish. Do you understand what that means, being brought up by the parish? For that, I will never forgive you.'

At last, she spoke. 'You are very proud, Mina. You are very like him, the way you walk and your actions. Do you want to know about your father? He was a proud, arrogant man, a man who wanted his own way at all costs. With him, the weak went to the wall, and I happened to be weak, where he was concerned anyway. What do you think he did when he knew I was expecting you? He sailed away. He was a fisherman and a Skyeman.'

I stared at her. I was too angry, too full of hate to grasp what she had just said. 'How many more of us are there?' I asked. 'If you lay down so easy to one man, you could do so to another, and another.'

Suddenly, I felt as if my teeth had been knocked down my throat by the blow from Aunt Kate's hand. 'I'm sorry I had to do that, Mina, but I had to stop you.' My hand flew to my mouth and when I drew it away, there was blood on it. My lips were bleeding. There were tears in Aunt Kate's eyes as she said, 'Your mother is a good woman. If she made a mistake, she has suffered for it.'

'Suffered for it. Her?' I threw back at Aunt Kate. 'Oh no, it was me who did all the suffering.' I was walking towards the door. I passed my two cousins who were staring at me open-mouthed. In the lobby, I picked up my coat and scarf, and returned to the sitting room to pick up my handbag. The shoes I had bought that afternoon were still lying on the couch where I had thrown them when I came in. 'I am going to stay at the hotel until the wedding. I know that can't be cancelled, but I assure you, I will pay for the wedding in full myself. I want nothing off any of you.'

Uncle Willie barred my way to the door. 'You are staying here. You are not in the habit of going to the hotel to sleep when you are on back-shift. This is your home until you are married.' I was still holding my handkerchief to my mouth. He turned to his two daughters. 'You two girls, start the supper.'

Without a murmur of dissent, Eva and Vera disappeared into the kichen. 'Come on into the bathroom, and I will look at that lip,' Aunt Kate said. 'I didn't mean to hit you so hard.'

'Just let me go to the hotel, Aunt Kate. I don't want to bother anyone.'

'That will do,' She grabbed my coat, threw it down on a chair caught my arm and drew me into the bathroom. I stood silently as Aunt Kate doctored my mouth. As we came out Aunt Ann was just leaving.

'Just a minute,' I rapped out. I had remembered something that she had said and I wanted to make sure I had picked her up right. 'Where did you say my father belonged to?'

'Skye.' She opened the outside door. I could feel the draught of cold air. 'And I wish he had stayed there,' she threw back. Skye. It was all I could think of. My father was a Highlander.

I didn't particularly want to know him and I didn't particularly care whether he lived or not, but it was enough for me to know I was half highland.

My two cousins and Uncle Willie had retired after supper. I was about to go upstairs when I turned into the sitting room. Aunt Kate was darning a sock. 'Aunt Kate, what was my father like?'

She hesitated. 'Well, for one thing, he could charm the birds off the trees, as the saying goes. Between his charm and his Highland brogue, a young girl hadn't much of a chance, especially if he took a fancy to her, as he did to your mother.'

'But why didn't he marry her?'

'I don't think she was strong enough to hold him.' Aunt Kate sighed. 'Perhaps if she had showed him, or can I say, demonstrated to him how much she really wanted him, it might have been different. But your mother was a very quiet reserved girl.'

'My mother was a fool,' I spat out.

'Mina, don't start that again,' Aunt Kate warned. 'Look at the time.'

I ignored her remark. 'Any woman that can't hold on to the man she loves is a fool and deserves to lose him. I despise her.'

Aunt Kate rose with a deep sigh. 'Your father spoke exactly like that over twenty five years ago when Willie asked him, in our little room, to marry your mother. He was too charming to use exactly the same words as you have done, but it meant just that. You are very like him, Mina. You haven't much time for people who are weaker than yourself.'

Chapter 35

I wrote to Bill explaining that the woman I had thought to be my Aunt, was in fact, my mother. I was illegitimate. After posting the letter I thought, perhaps he won't want to marry me now. If that had been in the back of my mind, I was going to be disappointed, it was not Bill's way. His letter was full of sympathy when it arrived. He wrote, 'I'm not marrying your mother, I am marrying you.'

Chapter 36

The week before my wedding was hectic. The staff gave me a
party and showered me with gifts. There were last minute
hitches to be sorted out. Perhaps if Ann had stayed away the
night before my marriage, I would have ignored her on the day
of the wedding. Bill and his brother Angus were to stay with her
on the Friday night.

The morning of my wedding was dull and cold. Everyone was
bustling about and couldn't understand why I was so calm. At
half past two everyone was away, except Uncle Willie and
myself, waiting for our taxi.

'I'm all dressed up here like a dish of fish,' he said sheepishly.
'But Mina, you look beautiful.' He sat down beside me on the
couch. 'I like that young man of yours. He will make a good
husband.'

I leaned against him. 'I hope I'm not making a terrible
mistake, Uncle Willie.'

'Oh no, dear, you could never go wrong with Bill.'

But that's not what I meant at all. I wasn't thinking of Bill,
I was thinking of Craig, but I didn't want to think of Craig, not
today. I was glad when the taxi arrived. As we arrived at the
church, I thought, Well, this is it?

I don't remember much of the service. I only know that when
we came out of the church, I was Bill's wife. We arrived at the
Reception Halls off George Street and, once inside, we were
lined up for the congratulations and good wishes. Then we
proceeded to the top table. The minister was standing beside me.
Relations came first after the bridesmaids and best man and then
the guests. Aunt Kate and Uncle Willie were coming forward as
my nearest relations. I turned. Among the guests was Ann.

'Will my mother please come forward and take her place as
my nearest relation?' My voice rang out clear.

A dead silence filled the hall. Everyone was looking at
everyone else. The minister looked at Aunt Kate, then at me.
He touched my arm. 'My dear, your Aunt Kate . . .'

I stopped him. 'My Aunt Ann is really my mother, Mr
Marshall, and as you asked for my nearest relation, it is she.'
I could hear the voices round about. 'Ann? Impossible.' I
heard someone else say, 'Well, well.'

I wasn't much interested in what happened after that, until
the telegrams were read. Angus was reading them. 'Here is the
last one from someone called Craig.' My heart was thumping

in my breast like a sledge hammer. 'The mountains and the Lochan and the Brae House are with you today,' he read, 'signed Craig.'

I wanted to rise off my chair and walk straight out of the hall. I felt like an alien in a strange land who neither knows the language nor the customs of the people he has come among.

The hall was being cleared and the band was tuning up. Bill and I had to take the floor for the first waltz and, as I have said before, Bill was a beautiful dancer. As he lifted me on to the floor, all eyes went to him and I glanced round the hall. I couldn't see my mother. She had gone. But I did see Aunt Kate glaring at me. She is very angry, I thought.

After the dance was finished, she came over.

'Why, Mina? Why did you do it?'

'She has been ashamed of me for twenty-five years, and I just wanted her, and her friends, to know I'm not ashamed of her.'

'That's not the reason, Mina. You must be very hurt inside when you want so much to hurt back.' She looked up at Bill. 'You have a wild one here,' she said.

'Don't worry, Aunt Kate, I'll tame her,' said Bill, and he put his arm round me. But Aunt Kate wasn't laughing. She was looking at Bill very strangely. 'You'll never tame this one. You are not strong enough.' Then I saw Aunt Kate stare at the door and give a gasp.

'Do you want to see a reflection of yourself, Mina? Well, there he is. That's your father standing there.' I rose. So did Uncle Willie. The man was tall, broad shouldered, dressed in a heavy fisherman's jersey. I couldn't see him properly from the position I was in. I was too far away. 'But how does he know about me and that I am being married today?'

'I told him,' Uncle Willie said. 'He lives in Aberdeen for so many months of the year, then returns home to Skye. This happened to be the time of year he is down here with the boats.'

'How did you find him?'

'It's not very difficult to find a fisherman in Aberdeen, especially Alister McRae, if you know where to look. Come on and meet him.'

My father was looking at me as I approached. 'Do you know who this is Alister?' Uncle Willie asked.

'Indeed, yes, and you look very grand.' His voice was musical, like all Gaelic speakers. His eyes had the look of a man who looks at vast distances. We shook hands and his grip was as firm as a rock. I turned to my Uncle, but he wasn't there. He was away talking to Angus.

'You are not at all like your mother,' my father said. I felt he was staring right through me. 'You are like the McRaes and I'm sure you have our guts too.' I didn't quite know if I liked this man or not. 'Where is your home to be?'

'Perthshire, in a small village there. Are you married?' I asked.

'I was, but she died. You have no stepbrothers or sisters, if that's to be your next question. I'll go now,' he said, 'I've seen you and from what I see, you look all right to me. I'll see you again, and the next time we meet, I will tell you all about Skye and the magnificent Cuillins. I know you will like that.'

We shook hands and he was gone. And it was time for Bill and I to leave too.

After I had changed into my going away clothes, I made a point of speaking to Edith and Rita and to their mother. Mary hadn't come to the wedding, nor had Jean. Mary was again in hospital. There was something wrong there.

The celebrations were over. We took the train from Aberdeen to Perth and changed there for Pirnhill Station. We were to spend the few days alone at The Mains before going to our own home in Turlum.

Chapter 37

The first few weeks of married life were the unhappiest I had ever known. I could not come to terms with marriage and all that went with it. I wept, stormed and beat against the traces. How Bill ever put up with it, I don't know. He tried talking to me. 'You surely are not so naive, as not to know what being married means.'

'I know what it means Bill, but I don't like it.'

'You haven't given yourself a chance. I've tried to be gentle with you, God knows, I've tried everything.' I knew he had. I knew his very gentleness was a reproach to me. I hated myself.

After three weeks of torture for both of us, his mother spoke to me one afternoon. 'I don't want to interfere between you two, but that is my son, Mina, and he is very unhappy, and so are you. I love you both and if you go on like this, your marriage will go on the rocks, so you'd better come to some kind of terms, before it's too late.'

I couldn't tell Bill's mother what was wrong, but surely there was someone I could talk to that would understand. It was then

I thought of Kate McDougall, the old char of the castle. I would go and see her. Kate was a wise old bird and maybe she would help me.

She was watching me closely as I entered her small house, after talking to Rachael outside it. I knew Rachael recognised me by the way she patted my clothes and cooed contentedly. 'And how is the bride?' Kate asked, after we had discussed a few general topics.

'Fine,' I replied, but didn't look at her.

'Then what are you doing here?'

'What do you mean? I have come on a visit to see you and Rachael.' I rose, 'but if you don't want . . .'

'Sit down lassie and tell old Kate what's wrong.'

As simply as possible, I told her. I couldn't come to terms with the physical side of marriage. 'There is someone else. Is that what you are trying to tell me?' I didn't answer. 'Does the man live about here?' I shook my head. 'Have you been with him?' I remained silent. 'Come on, Mina, have you been between the sheets with him?'

'Look, Kate,' I said at last, 'I came to you for help, not to give you a running commentary on my life, but if it's of any interest to you, I have never been between the sheets, as you put it, with any man except my husband.'

'And not very satisfactory with him, according to what you have told me.' said Kate. 'Well, I'm very fond of young Bill, and he doesn't deserve to be treated like that. You tell me there is someone else, so go home to Bill and until you come to terms with him, just shut your eyes and pretend it is the other man. It works you know, Mina. I can vouch for that.'

From that night on, I came to terms with married life and made Bill a very happy man.

Chapter 38

It was July when we got the invitation to Jean's wedding. Only relations and close friends. Bill, being a very reserved man, wasn't very keen on going as he felt awkward with strangers.

'You will like the Glen, Bill, I just know you will,' I said enthusiastically.

'I have no doubt. I have listened to you so often about this Glen, it must be paradise,' he laughed. And he agreed to go with me.

We arrived at Inverness on the 21st of July. Jean was getting married the next day. John McKenzie met us at the station and drove us back. I pointed out all the landmarks, but when we were passing the road leading to Drumoich, I remained silent and John took up where I left off. 'Up that road is Drumoich farm. My brother Donald and I work it together, all the fields you see parallel with the road belong to Drumoich.'

'Seems quite a big place,' Bill said.

'Donald isn't here just now, Mina. Did you know that he is in the Territorials? He's been called up on a fortnight's manoeuvers.' I wasn't much interested in Donald's manoeuvers.

'I don't think war is very far off,' said Bill, taking up the conversation, and they discussed the possibilities. At the Brae House Jean came running out with John's wife, Marjory. Jean kissed me warmly on the cheek and shook hands with Bill. I walked into the Brae House where Meg McKenzie was standing at the window. We embraced warmly and then Meg was shaking hands with Bill. 'Welcome to the Brae House. This was Mina's home too you know, so you are doubly welcome.'

We all sat round the table, Jean terribly excited and Marjory telling her to calm herself or she would be a wreck in the morning. 'With Craig giving me away, I'd better not. You know what he's like,' Jean said.

I had been lifting the fork to my mouth when my hand started to shake. His very name was enough to make my heart beat uncontrollably. It was John who broke the silence. 'Craig and Alex will be here tomorrow morning. They are at Drumoich tonight. Liz is not coming.'

I looked at Bill. If he had noticed anything, he didn't show it. We finished our meal and Marjory was saying she would take us to see the neighbours who, naturally, wanted to meet Bill. I must have been listening because I heard the footsteps outside before anyone else, and wasn't surprised when the outside door opened. Everyone turned as the handle of the kitchen door also opened. 'It's Craig,' Jean said.

His eyes flew to my face. It seemed as if there was no one else in the room but me. I thought for one awful moment, he was going to put out his arms to embrace me, so I moved, hurried to his side, took his hand and started to shake it. 'How are you, Craig, and this is Bill,' I said all at once. I felt I was choking, and my voice seemed very far away.

Craig looked down at me and whispered, 'Mina.' All the love that was inside me shone in my eyes. Craig seemed satisfied at what he saw. He sighed and turned away and held out his hand to Bill. The two men shook hands but Craig immediately turned back to me. 'Had a good journey up, Mina?'

I nodded. I was looking at Bill. His eyes went from Craig to me, back to Craig again and stayed there. It was John speaking that seemed to put everyone at ease. 'I thought you were taking Mina and Bill to the McAndrew's,' he said to his wife. Thankfully, I went to the lobby for my coat.

When we entered the McAndrew house, Peter made us welcome. 'Where's Mary?' I asked, expecting she would be up for the wedding.

'I'll have a word with you about that in a minute, Mina,' Mrs McAndrew said. 'Andrew,' she turned to her husband, 'a glass of whisky for Mina's husband first.' Mrs McAndrew handed me a cup of tea. 'Come ben to the parlour, Mina, I want to talk to you.' Wondering what was wrong, I followed. After the door shut behind us, Mrs McAndrew spoke. 'This isn't a time to be talking about trouble, with Peter getting married tomorrow, that's why I took you ben here. Mary has a spine complaint and has to lie on her back for six months.'

'Oh Mrs McAndrew, I'm terribly sorry. Poor Mary.' I felt shattered. 'When did this happen?'

'She hasn't been well for a long time. She was taken into the hospital once or twice, but they couldn't find anything wrong. At last, they have found out and treatment has begun. I will give you the name of the hospital in Glasgow before you go. I know you will want to go and see her.'

'Of course I will,' I reassured her.

'Her in-laws are the best in the world, but I feel they try not to worry me.'

I looked at this woman, who all through my childhood had kept me an outsider, and would have kept me from Mary, if she had dared. But Mary, with her independent spirit, had wished it otherwise. Standing, looking at this worried mother, I felt no animosity. Only a wish to ease the anxiety she must be feeling. 'Don't you worry Mrs McAndrew, I'll visit Mary as often as I can.'

Chapter 39

I watched Craig taking Jean up the aisle next day and felt very proud. He was so handsome in his black morning suit and white shirt and I had eyes for no one else. The service over, we went back to the McAndrew's, as there was no room for the two dozen guests in the Brae House. I was standing talking to Alex about his forthcoming marriage, when Craig came over. 'Mina, come over to the Brae House with me.'

'I can't do that Craig.'

'Why not? Jean and Peter are away, and Bill isn't here,' he said. I looked around. 'Where is he?' I asked.

'McAndrew wanted him to see round the farm.'

Alex looked at his brother. 'I've no doubt you had a finger in that pie.' he said. He looked at us both for a moment. 'You two should be on a desert island.'

'That's an idea,' Craig said, his face lighting up. 'Come on, Mina.'

We walked to the Brae House hand in hand. It never entered my mind that Bill could have been watching us from part of the farm, and I'm quite sure it didn't bother Craig. We entered the empty cottage. Craig slammed the door shut with his foot and I was in his arms. I could hardly breathe. I felt I had no longer the power over my body, that we were both losing control. I tried to push him away, but his grip was too tight. He lifted me bodily and entered the kitchen and laid me down on his mother's couch. Craig knelt down beside me, pushed my black hair away from my face and when he spoke his voice was soft and tender. 'What a strange thing this love of ours is,' he said. 'It's tender one minute and the next, wild and passionate. Then comes this awful longing for each other.'

I sat up. I was quiet inside. 'You could have done what you liked with me just now, Craig,' I said quietly.

He laughed, rose from his knees and sat beside me. 'I know. I was the strong one there. I see your marriage to this Bill has made no difference to our love, so I am content to wait.'

'Craig, I will never do anything to hurt Bill. I like and respect him too much. You are not jealous of him, are you?' I asked.

'We are too close for that, Mina,' he said, raising me up off the couch.

We were still embracing when Craig's mother came in. We didn't even hear the door open. 'Right you two,' she said. 'John sent me. Your Bill is back, Mina.' She was looking at me. 'And don't stand there with your arms round each other and me standing here.' We hadn't even jumped apart when the door opened. It just never entered our minds. 'Are you coming back with us, Meg?' I asked.

'No, I've had enough. I was sitting there in a cold sweat, watching you two, in case you made fools of yourselves, as you near did last night, barging in here like that, Craig, with your black eyes looking at no one but her. It was terrible altogether, Craig, and her green ones looking at you. No thanks, I'm going to bed.'

Craig was laughing heartily at his mother as he planked a kiss on her cheek. 'Mina's eyes are hazel, Mum, not green.'

'Well, you should know, you look at them plenty.'

Chapter 40

Everyone was dressed and ready for church next morning by ten o'clock. 'You don't have to go to church,' I said to Bill, 'just because they are going. It's the Wee Free and there is no organ or choir and the Gaelic service is a long one.'

'I've never been to a Gaelic service before, Mina, and I would like to go. What are you going to do?'

'Go up the hills,' I said simply.

I got no further than the Lochan. I sat down on the bank watching the wild duck swimming across the loch, leaving a V shaped wavelet in their wake. A skylark was singing like to burst above me. A grouse flew out of the heather making its way towards the hill. The sheep were eating the grass to my left, near the fank, where sheep are gathered for clipping. They were the young sheep, and I could see they had been clipped not so long ago. Eventually they would make for the hills too. Then I saw Craig. I rose, instead of making for the hill, and turned back to meet him.

It was I who spoke. 'Let's go back to the Brae House,' I said quietly.

Ten minutes later we entered it. 'Mina,' Craig said, sitting on the couch beside me, 'I feel this is the parting of the ways again.'

'Yes, Craig, only this time it's for a long, long time. It has to be, Craig. Every time we meet, it gets worse. Down there, I don't feel so bad, I feel I can cope, it's such a different world. But here, near you, it's hopeless. You see, don't you, what it's like when I'm here.'

'Yes,' Craig spoke quietly. 'When you are in the Glen, I can't stay away, and don't care if I never see Northfield again.'

'I know,' I said, 'and that's not good. Can you imagine what it would be like if I were here all the time?' I rose. 'I'll make some tea.'

'No, don't.' He rose and went to the dresser, lifted out a bottle of whisky, poured himself a glass and drank it in one gulp. 'Mina, I don't know where we will meet or how, but I do know, and feel it in my bones, that we will be together one day, and no one in between, not even Northfield.' He drew me to him and brushed my lips with his. The next thing I was aware of was the door opening and shutting. I saw him pass the window without even glancing in.

Chapter 41

Bill and I were back a fortnight when I opened the door to a knock and found my father standing outside. 'I told you I would come,' he said.

'Have you come from Aberdeen?' I asked.

'Yes, it's the first time I have done this run and I thoroughly enjoyed it.'

I was wondering why he had come, but my curiosity wasn't satisfied until Bill had returned and dinner was past. It had been a warm day and the kitchen window was wide open to the evening breeze. We were sitting at the table.

'Would you like to come down to the hotel for a drink, Mr McRae?' asked Bill.

'Alister is the name, and thank you but no. I've come to see Mina, so if you don't mind I'll not go out.' I knew Bill would be quite happy with that. He wasn't a drinking man.

'There is a war coming lad, and it's just round the corner,' Alister said. I shivered because I hated this talk of war. It only brought death and destruction and for what? To my way of thinking, nothing. Alister was looking at me. 'I'm a fisherman so I'll be in the thick of it,' he said. 'If anything happens to me, I would like you to go to Skye some day, to see my home.'

I looked at him across the table. 'What is Skye like, Alister?'

'Well, lassie, I can't tell you in words, not the way it should be told. You will perhaps get the words yourself after you go there.'

'Can't you try?' I said. 'Tell me about the Cuillins.' My eyes looked into his, as if to draw out of him what I knew was there, his love for Skye.

'Well,' his voice was thick with emotion. 'To the native, Skye calls them back, again and again. It is washed by the Atlantic. The greatness of the Cuillins in their beauty and majesty are indescribable. Man has to approach them with caution, and respect. If you are ever on a ridge of the Cuillins at sunset, especially Sgurr Alasdair, it's something you will remember all your life, but you will see them for yourself, I'm sure. I know you will love them and I know you will love Skye.' He sat back on his chair and gave a short laugh, as if embarrassed at showing his feelings.

'Can I sing the praises of Perthshire now?' Bill said with a laugh.

'Well Bill, you may sing the praises of Perthshire with pride, for not only in the north is there beauty. The magnificent scenery of Scotland, is to me anyway, the most beautiful in the world, and I have sailed to most countries.'

After a pause, because I had been waiting for the opportunity, I asked, 'Why didn't you marry my mother?' He didn't flinch at the sudden question, this strangely aloof and yet emotional man.

'Could you imagine anyone more unsuitable for me, than your mother? Could you imagine her tramping over the heather, working a croft, living perhaps a mile from her nearest neighbour?'

'Then why didn't you leave her alone?'

'I was young, away at sea for weeks on end, and when a girl . . .' he stopped. 'I am making excuses. The truth is, I didn't care enough.'

'Did you not care what happened to your daughter?' There were so many questions I wanted to ask.

'I didn't know I had a daughter,' he said, 'until Willie, your Uncle, told me just before you were married. Oh, I knew your mother was expecting you. Your Aunt Kate and Uncle Willie tried everything to get me to marry Ann, but it would never have worked out. She wouldn't think of going to Skye, actually she wouldn't even see me. So, two years later, I married another Aberdeen girl and took her to my house and we had five wonderful years together.' He gave a deep sigh, thinking over the past. 'I have no regrets,' he said at last.

Next day, Alister took his leave. During the time he had spent with us, my feelings towards him were very mixed. The answers he gave me weren't satisfactory, not to my mind. Although I had no love for my mother, I felt he should have more concern for the offspring that he knew he had so casually begotten. Up to the time he left, I had yet to think of him as my father.

Chapter 42

On the 3rd of September, 1939 we went to war with Germany. Overnight the village was turned into a garrison. At the back of the village, were fields belonging to one of the local farmers— I could see them from my kitchen window. Nissen huts sprang up in them like mushrooms, hidden from the sky by trees and camouflaged with green and brown paint. All through the night, we listened to the rumble of huge lorries and tanks, wondering where their destination was. Next morning we knew. We had a whole battalion of soldiers behind our village. It was the beginning of an army who were to be our guests until the end of the war. Some stayed a few months, others nearly a year, and so it went on. The village itself was good to the soldiers. We entertained quite a lot of them in our homes and, in return, they invited us to the village hall, which they had commandeered for a cinema and dance hall.

A lot of our men from the village volunteered or were called up. Jim Thompson, Rita's husband was one, but Edith's husband was a bricklayer and as such, was exempt. Bill came home one evening from work, and after dinner, we were sitting round the fire when Edith and Bob called. During the conversation, I heard Bill say to Bob, 'I went to the recruiting office in Perth today.' The squad was working at the station so I took the opportunity.'

I turned around from the sink where I was working. 'You didn't Bill . . . join up?' My voice was full of fear. Bill smiled, came over and put his arm round me. 'They wouldn't have me. Told me to go back to my work. Seemingly, a plate layer is an essential job, keeping the wheels of the ammunition trains on the rails.'

I gave a sigh of relief. When Edith and Bob left, I returned to the subject of recruitment. 'Bill, don't ever volunteer again. If anything were to happen to you . . .' I put my arms around his neck. He kissed the tip of my nose.

'Well,' he said, 'it will need to be the Local Defence or some other voluntary service.' It was later the Local Defence Volunteers which became known as the Home Guard. 'I must do my bit and that can be very exacting. I will have my work on the railway and the voluntary bit too. I will be out several nights a week.' I didn't care, as long as he wasn't called up.

The war was hotting up and travel became very difficult. I had kept my promise to Mrs McAndrew when we returned from Jean's wedding and had gone several times to see Mary in hospital, but with war breaking out, it became more difficult. The railways were full of goods trains carrying ammunition of every kind. There was a large ammunition depot below The Mains in the wood, on the doorstep of Pirnhill Station. Before long, Britain had become a fortress. Then in the summer of 1940 the bombs began to rain down on our cities, during what became known as The Battle of Britain, a battle which although we didn't know it then, was to save us from a German invasion.

That Autumn, my oldest son Alastair, was born. Jean wrote regularly. Both Peter and Jean were staying at the Brae House with Meg. In the spring of 1941 her son was born there. She never mentioned Craig in any of her letters, except to say that Liz had had a daughter, just before Alastair was born, never, in fact, mentioned any of the family, so it was something of a shock one day when I walked into Donald, dressed in a Sergeant's uniform.

I was on my way to have a chat with Edith. She and Rita lived at the bottom end of the High Street, while I stayed at the top end. I was pushing Alastair in front of me in his go-chair and passing the Public Hall when a voice called, 'Well, well, if it isn't Mina!'

'Donald!' I stared. 'What on earth are you doing here, and in uniform?'

'Trying to fight a war,' he said, beaming. I got here in the small hours of the morning, from somewhere in England.' The movement of troops had long ceased to keep us off our sleep, but what we did know, in that strange way civilians had of knowing things, was, that when the troops arrived at Turlum, their next move was embarkation.

'Would you like to come to the house for supper tonight?' I asked, 'or will you not be off duty? We stay at Number 14.'

'Yes, thanks. I'll manage. We are busy settling in at the moment, so I'll see you later.'

When Bill came home and was washing himself at the sink, I told him about Donald. 'Is that the chap who was up at the Castle?' he asked.

'Did you know about that?' I asked surprised.

'Yes,' he said, 'I knew about it. You can't do much in this

village without everyone knowing.' I smiled, amazed he had never said anything before.

Donald arrived and I watched the two men shake hands. 'I see you are in the Home Guard,' Donald said. Bill was in his uniform, as it was one of the evenings he had to attend Parade.

'Yes, I'm sorry I've to go out, but Mina will take good care of you. I've no doubt you two have a lot to talk about.' After Bill had left, I was conscious of Donald's eyes on me while sitting beside the fire. Alastair was asleep in his cot. I cleared my throat. 'Tell me, Donald, why you joined the Army? I know they don't call up farmers, so you must have volunteered.'

'I did. I was in the Terries. Remember I was away at camp one time you were up? So, when war broke out, well, I just enlisted, simple as that.'

'Are you trying to tell me Donald, you left Drumoich to join the Army? Well, I don't believe you, there is more to it than that.' I was watching him closely, and a hot flush crept over his face and his eyes dropped. 'Well, it's none of my business, of course.'

He sat silently, weighing up the situation. 'You will hear some day, I suppose, so I'm as well to tell you now. There was a bit of a mess.' He hesitated and he moved uneasily in his chair. 'Remember a girl, Ella Munro. Well, she got pregnant, and she blamed me. I'm not saying I didn't have something to do with it, but marriage with Ella . . . ? No thanks. Old Munro was going to take me to court, unless there was compensation.'

I knew Harry Munro. He was the type of man who would have robbed his own mother for a shilling and his daughter being pregnant to one of the McKenzies of Drumoich would be a God-send to Old Harry, especially if he saw pound notes flying around.

Donald continued. 'There was a family conference with Craig, of course, in the chair, and a devil of a row. Mother was terribly upset and the district buzzed, as you can imagine. 'Poor Ella,' they said, 'and only seventeen.' He gave a grin. 'At seventeen, she wasn't even a virgin. Craig was furious. I got a lot of yap from him about self control, etc. and it finished up with the family deciding—which means with Craig deciding— that if he bought my share of Drumoich, I would have some money to give Old Harry. Either that or marry Ella. I refused to marry her. I wasn't even sure if I was the father.' Donald rose and paced about the kitchen. 'So, I decided to join up. I like the Army. I've put in for a commission.' He sat down again.

'Donald, there is more to it than that. Craig just didn't buy your share of Drumoich because of what you have told me.'

'Well,' he continued, 'John was grumbling a bit that I wasn't doing my share. Thought he was getting the heavy end of the stick, or so he said anyway.'

'Is that all Donald?' He rose again and walked to the window. 'Damn these blackouts.' He was referring to the windows. During the war, strips of black paper were glued round the edges of the panes, a black blind was then drawn over this and heavy curtain material drawn across the full length of the windows to prevent any speck of light being seen from the sky.

He returned to his chair and sat down. 'No, it's not all,' he said. 'There was Jeannie McMillan from Hollybush.'

'I thought Jeannie McMillan,' I interrupted, 'was married and living in Inverness to . . . what was his name again?'

'Ferguson,' Donald answered. 'He has a small business going in the town. Well, Jeannie and he had split up and she was back in the Glen, and to cut a long story short, Ferguson was taking her back. They had no family.

'The irony of it was that what Ferguson couldn't do in four years, I did in as many months.' This seemed to amuse Donald no end, and he threw back his head and roared with laughter. 'When he arrived at Drumoich, I couldn't deny I was seeing Jeannie. We had been seen by too many people. He nearly killed me. That was the last straw. Craig acted and well, here I am.'

I sat and looked at Donald, seeing no remorse for the trail of misery he had left behind. Women meant little to Donald. He used them, and after they had supplied his needs, they were forgotten, until the next time. I remembered Jeannie McMillan and smiled. Years ago, I had been a victim of Jeannie's taunts and remembered it well. We were playing rounders in the playground and I got to the stance first—at least the ball did and it was I who had thrown it. She was furious.

'I'm not out,' she shouted.

'You are,' I said, 'I hit the stance.'

'You're a liar, Mina Forbes. All you orphans are the same— liars. Come on, Chris,' she turned to her pal, a Glen girl, 'don't play with them, they are a bunch of cheats.'

I just stood there, helpless, but an older girl, Irene Brown from Glasgow, who stayed with foster parents in Dalreich, sprang at her, caught her by the hair, threw her on the ground and after leaving Jeannie howling, turned her white face to me, saying, 'Come on, Mina, they are not worth bothering about.'

So, Jeannie had fallen victim to Donald's charm. I wasn't sorry. Coming back to the present, I asked, 'Do you think losing Drumoich was worth it, Donald?'

'I haven't lost Drumoich, Mina, it's mine and John's. At least it's John's until he gets a place of his own. That's how it was left by father.'

The evening had passed and I rose to make supper and lay the table. Then Alastair was whimpering and needing attention. When I returned from the bedroom, Bill had come home and was laying his rifle down carefully away at the far end of the kitchen. I hated that rifle. After supper, Donald returned to barracks with an open invitation to call whenever he wished. Later, I told Bill about our conversation. He listened without interruption, then asked quietly. 'That's the eldest brother that's bought Donald's share, isn't it?' I nodded. 'He must have plenty money, a farm of his own and a half share in another,' Bill continued. I wanted to talk of something else, I just didn't want Craig's name brought up.

'He isn't the oldest of the family,' I said hastily. 'Meg is. She and her husband have been in Canada for a number of years. Remember when we were at Jean's wedding? Her mother was talking about it. I only saw Meg once, that was the first time I saw . . .' I stopped.

'Saw who, Mina?' Bill was looking at me.

'Well, the McKenzie family. I was only eleven then.'

I turned away. Why did Bill just sit there, looking at me as if he wanted me to go on, or was it my imagination? 'I'll need to wash the supper dishes, Bill. It's getting late.'

Donald became a constant visitor and met all our friends. Edith and Rita started matchmaking as soon as they heard he was a bachelor, which didn't please me at all, although there was nothing I could do about it. We were all at Rita's one evening when her husband Jim was on leave, which called for a celebration. I saw Donald was making up to one of the village girls at the party and drew him aside. 'Look, I have to live with these people after you go away, and I don't want any little Donalds running around.'

'That's all right, Mina, if a girl throws herself at me, who am I to refuse her generosity?'

'Why don't you just get yourself a nice girl and settle down?'

'Once, I proposed to a nice girl and was turned down flat. I vowed then that no female would ever do that to me again, so now, I just take what I want.' I moved away. There was no use talking to Donald in that mood. I wanted him to visit his mother when he got leave, but he refused, saying, 'After the war when I'm back in Drumoich, will be time enough.' He didn't want her to know that he was billeted at Turlum.

The next time I saw him, he came in and threw himself into the nearest armchair. 'We are on the move. I'm not supposed to tell you that, as you know. Everything is hush hush. Troop movements must be concealed, so not a word. Of course, you know that without me telling you.'

I felt cold inside. 'When?' I asked quietly.

'Tonight. At midnight. When you get up in the morning there will be a lot of new faces on the street.'

'Where?'

'Now that I don't know. But the grapevine says it's to one of the ports.'

It was August, 1942 and there was bitter fighting going on in North Africa somewhere. If Donald's regiment was going to the ports, it meant one thing—embarkation. 'Please, be careful Donald.' Something forced the words out of my mouth.

He rose and stood beside me at the cooker. 'Don't tell me you are falling in love with me at last?' His tone was mocking. So were his eyes.

'Go and sit down and stop making fun of me.'

'What about you and Craig, Mina?'

My heart began to hammer, even at the mention of his name. 'Why bring that up?' I asked. 'I'm perfectly happy with Bill.'

'Of course you are. What girl wouldn't be happy with someone who loved her as Bill loves you. That's not what I meant.'

'Donald, my feeling for Craig will never change.'

'Nor his for you,' he cut in.

'With a war on,' I continued, ignoring his remarks, 'we should just live from day to day and let tomorrow look after itself.'

That night in bed, I lay awake listening to the rumble of traffic. The battalion was on the move. I began to fall asleep about four o'clock. The traffic was still rumbling past but, as I dropped off, it was coming into the village. The new regiment had arrived.

Then came some bad news, first a telegram that Uncle Willie had died. Bill went to the funeral for me, and on his return told me my father was dead, believed drowned at Dunkirk.

I remembered hearing all about Dunkirk on the wireless, about the gallant fleet of boats of all shapes and sizes who went out from Britain to help evacuate the British Expeditionary Forces from Dunkirk. The men who manned these small boats snatched over three hundred thousand French and British soldiers from certain death.

'Your Uncle went down to the docks, not long after the evacuation.' Bill told me. 'The men who returned to tell the tale said that the last they saw of your father and his mate was in the water. There was nothing they could do, but try to get the soldiers in their boats back to safety.'

So, my father had been in the thick of it, just as he said he would. I wondered why I hadn't heard, after saying he would keep in touch and now I knew. I felt sad about my father, but after all, I scarcely knew him. 'I'm sorry about that, Bill. I believe if I had come to know him, I would have liked him. He was so different from my mother. He had guts, he wouldn't have been a fisherman if he hadn't and, of course, he was a highlander.'

'Will you go to Skye now, Mina? He wished you to.'

'If he had lived, I might have, Bill, but not without him. Now that he is no longer here, I don't think so. I don't want another rebuff. I learned my lesson among my mother's people. I'll not make that mistake again.

Chapter 43

A few weeks later, Alastair became ill. Nurse Chisholm was in every day to see him and Dr Anderson as often as possible. I will never forget those two kind people. Their attention was far above that of duty. Friends called, sympathised and left. Bill's mother couldn't do enough for us, but I clung to Nurse Chisholm and Dr Anderson. My constant plea was to 'Save my son.' I scarcely closed my eyes, afraid of what I would find when I awoke. Bill was a bulwark of strength, yet he must have been suffering as much as I was.

It was the first week of September. Autumn was mild that year. I left Bill's mum with Alastair and went to get the rations. I had to pass our church on the way. It was Bill who was the churchgoer. I would go with him, more out of duty than anything else, but this morning, seeing the church door open, I walked in. The cleaners were busy in the main body of the church and when they saw me, they immediately asked after Alastair. I shook my head. 'Just the same,' I answered. They must have sensed what I was going to do and disappeared into the vestry.

I went forward to the Communion Table, knelt down and prayed. 'Save my son, please. Please God, if you want a life, take mine, but not Alastair's, he hasn't lived. Let him live God, let him live.' My face was wet with tears as I rose from my knees, left the church and arrived back at the house. I had forgotten my shopping.

That evening, about eight o'clock, Dr Anderson came in. 'Sorry I'm late, I've surgery,' he said. 'Now, how's the wee fellow?' He went over to the cot and took one long, serious look at Alastair. 'I'm taking him to hospital,' he said gently and lifting Alastair, wrapped the blankets round him and made for the door.

'I'm coming too, doctor,' I said and grabbed my coat from the lobby.

Out in the street, I opened his car door. 'Get in,' he said hurriedly, indicating the back seat, 'and take Alastair on your knee.' Bill was at my side helping me. When the baby and I were comfortable, he went and sat in front beside the doctor.

The hospital was several miles away, but we arrived in record time. Still holding my son, I entered the hospital and then Dr Anderson took over. 'You two wait here. Give me the child.'

We waited for hours. Nurses, sisters, porters passed us in the corridor and we didn't know what was happening. We only knew that wee Alastair was in the theatre. It was eleven o'clock when Dr Anderson came out of one of the wards. He looked a tired exhausted man, so was the surgeon who came out with him. He told me, 'We have done all we can. You will know by this time tomorrow if it has been a success.'

Next day seemed to drag on and on. Nurse Chisholm, came in during the afternoon to tell me the doctor had just left for the hospital. It was a long two hours later before the bell rang and Dr Anderson was standing outside. I didn't speak, just nodded to him to enter. He stood in the centre of the kitchen, beside the table. 'Alastair is going to be all right,' he said and the relief on his face was nearly as great as our own.

I threw myself at Bill, sobbing with sheer joy and relief. He held me close to him whispering, 'There, there, Mina, just you cry away.' We were closer together at that moment than we had ever been. When I lifted my head from Bill's shoulder, Dr Anderson had slipped away.

Chapter 44

After a month in hospital, I took Alastair home and we had a small celebration, with Bill's mother, Rita and other friends. During the evening the door bell rang. On opening the door I saw the local policeman standing outside. 'Hallo, John,' I said, 'come in.'

'No thanks, Mina,' he said solemnly, 'is Rita here?'

'What's the matter?' I could just whisper.

'Jim has been killed, but for goodness sake, don't tell her. Send her out and I'll talk to her.'

John was more of a friend than a policeman. I nodded hurriedly and went in for Rita. Poor Rita; from a happy, carefree, laughing girl, she was turned into a heartbroken woman. Edith and I tried to console her, but for months we seemed to be fighting a losing battle. Finally, we persuaded her to take a job, which seemed to ease the situation a bit. Then, at the end of March 1943, word arrived from Jean that Donald had been killed in North Africa. She wrote a long letter about him but most of its contents I knew. What I didn't know was that he had made Craig his next of kin, which meant that Craig now owned Drumoich, as well as Northfield. John was to remain at the farm if he wished, and if not, he could get a manager for Drumoich until his son was old enough to take over Northfield. I also got another shock that year. Aunt Kate died, and Jack was taking his two sisters out to America. Before they left, they came to Turlum to say goodbye. The war dragged on for another two years, but in 1945 on April 30th, Hitler committed suicide and by September the war was over.

The following Spring my twin sons were born. James arrived first and fifteen minutes later came Andrew. Alastair was now growing into a fine sturdy lad at school and no one seeing him playing football, and getting into all the scrapes boys get into, would think that a few years ago he had been at death's door. The twins grew like mushrooms and were three years old when I decided that my sons were going to have a better chance in life than I had had. I remembered Uncle Dunk telling me that the Glen would never hold me. Well, Turlum village would never hold my sons.

I put it to Bill one evening after the children were in bed. 'How would you like to live near Glasgow or Edinburgh?' I asked, watching his face.

'Whatever for?' he asked.

'Well, there are Universities there.'

'Well, what has that to do with us?'

'Not us, Bill,' I said, 'for the boys.'

Bill laughed. 'Honestly, Mina, the things you think of. Alastair is only eight and the twins are only three. Now, if you had said you wanted to stay in the Glen, I wouldn't be surprised, but Glasgow or Edinburgh . . .!' He dismissed the whole idea with a wave of his hand.

'I mean it, Bill. I want to go before the twins start school.' That evening was the beginning of many arguments, but I couldn't shift him. He was determined not to go, but I was just as determined that he would. The moment I brought the subject up, he would bury himself in his paper and refuse to discuss it.

Our friends were on Bill's side. His mother said little, but I knew she strongly disapproved of my plan. Then one evening, exasperated by my constant nagging, Bill exploded. 'Why, Mina, must you keep harping on about this subject? I'm sick and tired.'

'So am I, Bill, so let's discuss it rationally.' I sat down beside him. 'What is here for the boys? They are miles from an Academy and over fifty from a University. So, what's the alternative? We take them away from school at fourteen.' This was the leaving age then. 'They go to the labouring or, if they are lucky enough, to a trade. And what happens? They work on Turlum estate, and failing that, they become farm labourers. No thanks, Bill, you are not subjecting our sons to that kind of life.'

'What if our sons aren't clever enough to get on in school, and they want to become labourers and tradesmen?' Bill argued in that pigheaded manner that he took on occasionally.

'Then, Bill, they will have my blessing. But don't you see, I am giving them a choice? I couldn't do that here. For one thing, we don't have the money. Down South, we would be nearer schools, colleges and universities. Travelling would be cheaper, and when they are ready to work, jobs will be easier to come by, because the West of Scotland is the Industrial Belt.' Gradually I won Bill over. It took me eighteen months, and then another six months for Bill to get his transfer from Perth to Glasgow.

A house was the biggest bogey, but we got one in the end. An elderly couple wished to return back to Perthshire where they had originally belonged and an exchange was required. I saw it advertised in the daily papers and I immediately set the wheels in motion. Three months later, we were ready to flit. I hadn't seen our new home, but Bill had. It was a modern four apartment Council house, about twelve miles from Glasgow in the

small mining town of Glenburn. To come from a small sleepy
village in the Perthshire foothills to a fair sized bustling mining
community was certainly a big change.

We arrived about five o'clock on a March evening. The boys
had never seen a coal bing before, and wanted to know how
'dross', as they called the bings, got piled so high up. 'Look
Mum,' Andrew said, as we approached our new home, 'there
are more over there and there.'

He was right. From my new house, I could see three coal
bings about a mile apart. The nearest was only a quarter of a
mile from our door. There may have been a view beyond, but
the bings were our foreground. It was all very different from
Perthshire and the Glen.

The first thing to do was to get the furniture and carpets, rugs
and linoleum into place. We needn't have worried about that.
Before the first piece of linoleum was placed on the floor, a
group of women arrived, followed by several men. Less than an
hour later, my furniture was in place, tea was being made and
bread and butter sandwiches appeared as if by magic. A hoard
of children played 'tig' round the removal van with my boys
joining in. Bill went to the nearest pub and bought a bottle of
whisky for the men and sherry for the women. My home was
baptised and we were welcomed into the community. Never
have I known such kindness as was shown to us that day by
people who were absolute strangers, not only in kith and kin,
but in kind.

Ninety per cent of the community of Glenburn were miners
and The Miners Welfare Hall was the focal point of the
community. The 'Welfare' as it was best known, had one huge
hall for dancing and concerts, a smaller hall with a billiard or
pool table, which was very popular, and a darts and games
room for cards and dominoes. The Women's Section of the
Welfare was also very popular. Once a week, the women held
their meetings in the main hall, where every topic concerning
the community was discussed, especially the children and their
men folk. Bill and I, although we were outsiders, were made
very welcome at this centre from the very outset.

It didn't matter to the miners, or their wives, who you were
or what you were. You were just accepted as one of them. As
one woman said to me, 'You say you are not a miner's wife—
well, it makes no odds to us. You see, lassie, we are all Jock
Tamson's bairns.' That to me, is the basis of the miners'
philosophy, and my admiration for the community is great.
Because of the miner we have heat and light, but have we

stopped to think of the men who mine the coal? Every lump we burn has to be hacked out of seams. In those days the seams were sometimes, only eighteen inches high, which meant the miner had to lie on his stomach to get at the coal, or stand in water for hours on end. If the powers-that-be had been made to work down in the bowels of the earth at the coal face for only a week, the miner would have been the highest paid man in the country, even then. But they've had to wait.

My children settled in and enjoyed their school life. Bill, although rather reserved at first, was soon thawed out by the many small kindnesses shown us. Not long after our arrival, there was a function in the Welfare, where I met Janet Gillespie and her husband Charles, who were soon to become great friends. Janet was about my own age and she reminded me very much of Edith, being friendly and warm. Her little daughter Fiona was a lovely blonde child about the same age as the twins. Her father had been a miner and her husband, Charles, worked like Bill, on the railway. He was an entirely different sort of person from his wife, fun loving and liking to be part of good company. I never ever thought of having company in my home without asking Charles. He was the life and soul of any party.

But even in Glenburn, I came up against the past. I attended the Welfare regularly, and one night at one of our meetings, the speaker had finished a discussion about unwanted children. At our tea break, it became our main topic of conversation and a very interesting discussion developed. Janet wasn't there that night, but when we met next day, I mentioned the discussion in the Welfare the previous evening.

'Well,' Janet said, her head to one side, 'I don't know much about them, but it's dreadful that there should be unwanted children. What kind of parents do that kind of thing anyway, throwing their children, their own flesh and blood, to the mercy of the public?'

'What,' I said quietly, 'if the parents aren't married?'

'Well, perhaps that's different. Anyway, our parents didn't abandon us, did they? I can never thank mine enough for their love. You didn't say if your parents are alive or not, did you, Mina?' she said after a pause.

'My parents are dead, Janet.' My chance to tell her the truth about my parents had gone. I had also never, at any time, discussed Craig's love for me nor mine for him. That was too deep, too poignant. I had stopped writing to Jean in the Glen and Mary in Rothesay. What was the use, it was only reminding me of the Glen, and the home-sickness, even after all this time, was sometimes overpowering.

Bill often asked me why I didn't go up to the Glen. 'You should,' he would say, 'and take the boys with you.' But I couldn't. I wouldn't be twenty four hours in the Glen, before Craig would know. To meet him now, would be asking for trouble. I knew if Craig and I were to come together again, it would have to be because we had every right to do so. If we never met again, we had the memory of our love. And that, no one could take away.

Chapter 45

My boys were growing up into fine sturdy lads. Alastair was the studious type, but put him in a football park and he imagined himself a genius. 'No one can beat me in the tackle, Dad,' he would say proudly. The truth was, no one dared tackle him, they were afraid of being kicked off the field. He liked the school, especially the Academy. I saw the potential and encouraged him in every way and by the time he was fifteen (the school leaving age had risen by one year), I knew Alastair would go to one of the Glasgow Colleges or University.

The twins were entirely different. For one thing, they were twins and if their school mates attacked one, the other immediately defended. I was roasted with frustration by mothers coming to my door. 'Mina, what are you going to do with those terrible twins of yours? My Johnny has a bleeding nose and he says it was your twins.' Another mother would have her son with her. 'Look what your twins have done to my George,' pointing to his bruised face and legs. And so it went on. I smacked them, kept them in or sent them to bed, according to the size of the bruises or amount of blood drawn. There was nothing else I could do, short of chaining them to a chair, but let them run or fight to get rid of their energy, keeping my fingers crossed all the time and hoping for the best.

James was the clever one. He didn't study like Alastair. He didn't have to, it was all there. He left the Primary school as its Dux, another potential University student. Andrew was very different from his twin brother, not interested in school which he disliked intensely. He refused to learn his lessons, would hand his books to James, tell him what he wanted done and slip out to play. When he entered the Academy, the story was the same, except in the woodwork room or the metal room. There, Andrew shone above his brothers, especially in metal.

It was after Alastair had gone to the College that I noticed that Bill now tired easily and didn't want to take me out as often as formerly. I spoke to Janet about it, but she shrugged it off saying, 'Don't worry about Bill, Mina, he is a healthy looking man.' This lulled my fears for a short time, but all the same I urged Bill to see a doctor. He refused to do this, insisting there was nothing wrong. He just needed his holidays.

We went to Perthshire—to The Mains—on holiday that year. Bill's mother liked the boys. She was getting old, nearly eighty, and I noticed she didn't walk very far from the cottage these days. A few days after our arrival, when Bill was helping his brother about the small farm, the twins with them, I was washing the utensils and the girls were with Grannie on the porch at the front of the house, one of them said, 'There is someone coming out of a car and Bill is talking to him. Wonder who that can be?'

I put the baking bowl away and walked over to the window. I gave a gasp. Outside was Alex McKenzie. 'You know him?' Dot asked. I nodded and kept looking at Alex. He was older, of course, and stouter, growing bald, but I would have recognised him anywhere.

My heart thumped madly. I wanted to ask a million questions all at once—about Craig, about the Glen, but instead, politely held out my hand. 'How are you, Alex? You look well,' and we shook hands.

'I'm fine. The years have been kind to you, Mina, I see.'

'What brought you down here?' Bill asked.

'Well,' Alex began, 'I'm building up my dairy herd and saw in the *Farmers' News* that a farmer was selling off some of his stock. Gibson at Bridgend Farm. Seeing I was in the district I called at Turlum only to be told you were staying somewhere near Glasgow.'

'You and Mina will want to exchange news, after all these years. And she will be wanting to know all about the Glen.'

'Well, that's what I'm here for,' Alex cut in. 'There have been a lot of changes, Mina.'

I asked him, 'How is your mother?'

'My mother died, five years ago.'

'I'm sorry, Alex, really sorry. She was a fine woman. And Sheila, your wife?'

'Sheila is fine and I have a fine son and daughter now, or did you already know that?'

'No, I haven't heard from the Glen since Donald was here and that is fifteen years ago.'

'Why didn't you tell us Donald was living with you, Mina,' he said suddenly. 'It wasn't until we got news of his death and his belongings were sent home that we found letters among them, from Bill and a girl from this village.'

'Donald didn't live with us, Alex. He was in barracks behind the village, and it was his express wish that I wasn't to tell any of you where he was. That's the reason I stopped writing to anyone in the Glen. Anyway, that was one of the reasons.'

'Well, the other reason was obvious, Mina. It was Craig, wasn't it?'

Craig. I tried not to show any great interest and to sound casual as I said, 'Tell me, how is Craig?'

'His wife is dead.' I just sat and stared. My throat seemed closed. I tried to swallow but couldn't. 'She died six months ago. Cancer. She died in hospital and Craig certainly did his duty by her in every way possible. He has nothing to regret there.'

At last I found my voice. 'I'm glad he did, for his sake.' By now the others had left us alone, and I went on less quietly, 'What about his family? Are they at Northfield?'

'His son John is there—he's not married yet. Wilma, his daughter, is going out to Australia next month, to be married to a chap from Inverness. Craig is at Drumoich. McNaughton, the Manager who farmed Drumoich until John was ready to take over Northfield is with John now, showing him the ropes. Craig is finished with Northfield, Mina, it's John's now. It has caused too much suffering and unhappiness for both you and Craig for him to want anything more to do with it.'

He turned me towards him. 'He still feels as you do. That will never change. I envy you and Craig, and I always did. What is it between you that your feelings for each other have withstood all this time and the separation?.' He drew a deep breath. 'Remember the night of Mary McAndrew's wedding, when I stopped you both leaving the barn? I often wonder what would have happened if I had allowed you both to go.'

'I can answer that, Alex,' Suddenly, I felt I could talk to this man. 'We would have gone to the Brae House and I would have become Craig's mistress. You know what that would have involved? Misery to his wife, his mother and to the whole family in fact. I would have become an embittered woman. As it is, I am a happy, contented wife and mother. I have the love of a good man, Alex. Another thing, if I had had a child by Craig, I would never have forgiven myself for bringing an illegitimate child into the world. Perhaps, if we had grown up in this day and age, it might have been different. Who knows?' I was able to tell him clearly and honestly because I had had all those years to answer the questions myself.

He listened to me in silence, and seemed to be weighing up his words very carefully. 'I doubt if you would have been different, Mina, even in this day and age, as you put it. There is one thing I'm sure of, that it would have made no difference to Craig if you had been his mistress, as long as he had your love.' He gave a small laugh. 'You know, he never really forgave me for stepping in that night. Do you know what he said to Liz and me when he got home to Northfield?'

Without waiting for me to speak he went on. 'He told us, we could remain at Northfield, just as long as we minded our own business and didn't interfere with his way of life. We both knew what he meant, of course. If ever you came and lived in the Glen, any pretence at married life between him and Liz would be out, and I would need to keep my thoughts and opinions to myself. Then came Jean's wedding and, as I myself was getting married shortly afterwards, I wasn't bothering what happened between you two. I was leaving Northfield. But poor Liz, she just had to wait to see what was going to happen. You went back to Aberdeen after the wedding and you haven't returned.'

'Mina.' He paused. 'I want to tell you something before I finish. In hospital, Liz was being visited by us as much as possible. Well, Sheila and I arrived this certain evening with minutes to spare before visiting time was over, so we got Liz to ourselves. She was more cheerful, more like herself than I had seen her for some time. When we were coming away, she gripped my arm. "If ever you see Mina Forbes, tell her I hope she will get her life's desire." I knew what she meant and I said I would, so here I am, to tell you in person.'

I remained silent for some minutes. Craig was free, but I wasn't. As long as Bill lived, I would never see Craig. I owed Bill that, in return for the love he had given me and was still giving me. If I died before Bill there would be no problem, and he would never know of the longing and yearning that never eased with the passing of time. As I listened to Alex, I knew it was the same with his brother.

'Alex, don't tell Craig where we are. I don't want Bill ever to guess.'

'Afraid I can't do that Mina,' Alex said. 'By the time I get

back and see Craig, it will be to say God speed. He is going to
Australia to see Wilma married. When he comes back, it's here
he is coming, to see you. There is no use me telling him I don't
know where you áre, there will be plenty in this village who
know.'

'But what about Bill? Alex, he must never know,' I said
anxiously.

'Are you sure he doesn't know already, or hasn't at least
guessed?'

'How can he guess, unless he thinks it's you. Maybe that's
why he just left us on our own.' I burst out laughing at the
expression on Alex's face.

'I know what you are going to ask next,' he went on, smiling
at me. 'What about the Brae House?'

I nodded, returning the smile. I couldn't speak as the
memories of Uncle Dunk flooded over me. How proud he would
have been of Bill and my three sons, and how sad he would have
been about the love Craig and I had for each other—a love that
even Uncle Dunk would not deny was genuine, deep rooted and
lasting.

'Well,' he said, 'it's still standing. Peter and Jean wanted to
use it as a store room for grain, but . . .'

'What!' I swung round looking at Alex. 'How dare they do
such a thing to the Brae House? How dare they?' I was trembling with anger and the tears rushed to my eyes. 'Alex, please,
please, tell Craig not to allow them to do that. Not the Brae
House, oh no, not the Brae House. Not to the Brae House.' The
tears spilled over and poured down my cheeks.

'Mina, you didn't allow me to finish what I was going to say.
Now listen. Craig has bought the Brae House outright from the
Estate. I was just going to tell you that. The Brae House is safe.'

'Did you give Mina all the news about the Glen?' Bill asked,
as he returned.

'Oh yes, brought her up to date with everything.' Grannie
joined the conversation by saying, 'I don't know why you don't
all go up for a holiday. It's lovely up there. Their father,' she
said, between mouthfuls, nodding towards Bill and Angus,
'belonged to Sutherland, and the boys have never been up
there.'

'We will make it some day,' Angus smiled at his mother.

Chapter 46

After our holidays, the weeks seemed to fly. The Glenburn community were preparing for the Festive Season, always a grand affair. Children's parties had to be arranged, old people's parties, dances and parties for all ages. Then came the evening that every Scotsman awaits—Hogmanay. You have to be in a community like a mining one during the Festive Season to appreciate it properly. They're wonderful people, living as they do with danger every day, yet they amazed Bill and myself by the way they could let themselves go when they set out to enjoy themselves. There is an atmosphere of gaiety, happiness and goodwill that is hard to beat anywhere.

I was rummaging through drawers one morning, looking for something suitable for the children's Fancy Dress Dance. Being a member of the Welfare Committee, I had my share to do and enjoyed it very much. I had just come downstairs when I noticed the postman had been. There was a letter on the mat. Picking it up, I noticed it was from Australia and, with trembling fingers, tore it open, then went into the sitting room and sat down. It was Craig's first letter to me for many years, not a love letter, I didn't expect it would be. He simply wrote of his wife's death, his daughter's marriage and how he saw her and her husband settled on their own fruit farm. He wrote of the intense heat and of how he wouldn't much care to live there. He was longing for the Glen and couldn't understand how I had lived for so long away from it. He told me that he had got my address from Alex, after his return from Turlum, just before leaving for Australia. He was returning after three months and would like to see me, if that was possible, sometime in the last week of January.

I showed the letter to Bill that evening. He took a long time to read it. Actually, he read it twice. When he spoke at last, handing me back the letter, he was watching me closely. 'You should get him to call, Mina.' I remained silent.

'Well, don't you want to?' he asked, 'After all, he is your friend.'

'Yes Bill, I know, but do you want him here?'

'Is there any reason why I shouldn't?'

I felt my face flush hotly and as I looked at Bill, I saw he was still watching me closely. Of course I wanted to see Craig. All the years of separation had not altered my feelings for him and I knew it was the same with him. Alex had told me that.

And his letter, although far from being a love letter, had told me so too. Every line had its meaning and assurance that he still loved me, especially the line where he asked how I could stay away from all I loved.

I was very much aware of Bill's attitude and his lack of enthusiasm, for usually when I said friends were visiting us, he was delighted, jumping up off his chair and going to the sideboard to make sure the whisky bottle was full. That night when I was answering Craig's letter, I turned to Bill who was reading his paper. 'I'm answering Craig's letter Bill, do I invite him here or not?'

He waited for what seemed an age before answering and I was about to repeat my question when he said, 'If you invite him here, Mina, I will make him very welcome for your sake.' He rose and turned on the television.

This was not like Bill. I opened my mouth to say so, when something stopped me. I don't know what it was. 'I'll tell you what, Bill,' I said, 'we won't invite Craig just now, but I'll tell him we will go up to the Glen this coming summer. How is that?'

Bill nodded. 'That will be fine.'

'After all,' I said, 'the boys have never been to the Glen. They might not want to, but you and I will go.'

Bill smiled at my enthusiasm. 'We will do whatever you want, Mina.'

But there was a lot to happen before the summer ever came.

Chapter 47

A few days before Christmas, I had been shopping in Glasgow and I arrived home, tired and footsore, just in time to make Bill and the boys' dinner. Alastair was in his final year at College and July would see him through. He already had offers of positions with several English companies, including one which interested him, just outside London. James was now in his fourth year at the Academy and Andrew was leaving school at Easter. I noticed that Bill, when he came home that night, didn't look well and ate very little.

'Are you feeling all right?' I asked anxiously.

'I think I'm taking the cold, that's all,' he said.

'I wish you would see the doctor. You haven't been yourself lately, and I don't like that cough.'

'Och, I'm fine, Mina. It's just the cold. You fuss too much.'

But still I worried, especially when he went to bed much earlier than usual. Janet called that evening, and a few minutes after Bill went up, I told her that I was worried about Bill. 'He isn't well, hasn't been well for a while and refuses to see a doctor.'

'Well,' she said, 'why don't you wait until Saturday. He usually lies longer when he isn't working, doesn't he? Phone Dr Thompson then, and he will give him a check-up and you will be able to put your mind at rest.'

'I'll just do that, Janet. It's hopeless trying to get Bill to go to the doctor.'

'They are all the same,' Janet laughed. 'Charles is like that too, stubborn.'

We changed the subject and, instead, discussed the Christmas festivities which seemed to be going along smoothly.

But next morning, I was awakened by Bill, moaning softly beside me. I switched on the light beside the bed. His face was wet, with beads of sweat forming on his brow. I leapt out of bed, glancing at the alarm clock. It was only half past six.

'What's wrong, Bill?' I asked anxiously.

'I feel awful,' he answered weakly.

I grabbed my dressing gown, shoved my feet into slippers and ran out of the room, flew downstairs and opened the front door. The cold frosty morning struck me on the face and my cheeks tingled as I made my way to the telephone kiosk at the street corner, about one hundred yards away, and 'phoned Dr Thompson. Arriving back at the house, I ran upstairs to Bill. He was breathing heavily, as if he had just run a great distance. I woke the boys, went downstairs and started to make a cup of tea. The boys came down a few minutes later, half asleep and grumbling about having to be up so early.

'What's wrong, Mum?' Alastair asked. He had been looking at my face while the twins were busy talking about getting up in the middle of the night.

I explained about their Dad. 'I've 'phoned the doctor and I don't think he should be long.' I tried to sound matter-of-fact, but there was an ice-cold hand clutching my heart.

'What is it Mum? What do you think?' James asked.

'Well,' I hesitated, 'perhaps just a bad bout of 'flu. Let's wait and see what the Doctor says.'

Dr Thompson arrived soon after and went upstairs with me

at his heels. I waited nervously while he examined Bills' chest. When he had finished, he signed for me to follow him.

'What's the matter with him, Doctor?' My mouth was dry for fear of his reply. He was writing out a prescription. 'Your husband has pneumonia. I think I'll be able to confirm this when I come back.'

I opened the door and let him out. As I shut the door, I leaned against it. Pneumonia was a dangerous illness, I knew, but not usually fatal in this day and age. When the twins left at half-past eight, I went upstairs again. Bill was asleep, so I started my housework, more to keep myself occupied than anything else until the doctor arrived back as promised. When he was downstairs again, he walked into the sitting room and spoke quietly and kindly. 'Mrs Southall, your husband has double pneumonia and pleurisy. He will need very careful nursing for the next week or two. Do you think you can manage that?'

'Just tell me what I have to do, Doctor,' I said, thankful now that things weren't even worse.

'Good,' he remarked. 'If at any time you think you can't cope, I'll try and get him into the Cottage Hospital.'

'No, Doctor,' I said firmly. 'I'll nurse Bill.' He looked at me carefully and then, as if satisfied, he nodded. 'Good morning,' he said and was gone.

From that moment on, I became a dedicated nurse to Bill. I couldn't have done it alone of course, but with the help of Janet and my neighbours, I was able to cope, and between us all, Bill was in the best of hands. At Christmas I tried to look as cheerful as possible for the sake of the boys, who were a great comfort to me, as was Catherine Brown, Alastair's girlfriend. But as the New Year drew nearer, I knew it would be very difficult to keep up a brave front.

Hogmanay arrived. What a difference from former years when we'd had all our friends and neighbours around us with music blaring from the radiogram, or else the television on to watch the Hogmanay programme.

The doctor had ordered absolute quiet, and all our friends and neighbours observed this. Catherine and Alastair said they would sit with Bill and give me a rest, but I refused. I wanted Alastair to go to Catherine's home. He had been invited to first foot her parents, and I couldn't have my sons sitting around after midnight. They were too young to be involved in illness, and had friends who were expecting them. For the first time in years, I went to bed before the New Year bells, but Bill was restless that night, and I barely slept for fear he needed me.

I rose early on New Year's morning. Alastair hadn't returned.
He was probably staying with Catherine's parents, but I had
heard the twins come in about four o'clock. The front door bell
rang and I opened the door to find Dr Thompson on the step.
'A Good New Year, Mrs Southall,' he said. 'I was in the
vicinity, so I thought I would call. Then it's home to bed, I
hope.' I went into the sitting room and looked at the time, eight
o'clock on New Year's morning. A few minutes later, he had
seen Bill and said to me, 'I have some good news. He's past the
worst now and if this progress continues, he'll be able to get up
in a week or so for an hour. Of course, that all depends on his
progress.'

'Doctor, I'm grateful for all you've done,' I said, with a sigh
of relief.

'I have more to say, Mrs Southall,' he continued. 'Your
husband, as I've said, is recovering from pneumonia and
pleurisy, but on further examination, I see he has also developed
acute bronchitis and emphysema. He will never again be able
for work—heavy work that is. It's 'light' work only from
now on.'

I stared in horror at the doctor. I had heard of these dreaded
illnesses, indeed, one doesn't live in a mining district without
knowing and seeing the effects of coal dust on the lungs, and to
me emphysema meant the same thing. The lungs were affected
and unless the heart was very strong, it could be fatal. 'Doctor,'
I said, 'Bill is only forty-eight. How did he contract this?'

'Illness doesn't attack a specific age my dear. We're all
vulnerable. But if he continues as he's doing, there's no reason
why he shouldn't be back at work in about six months.'

When the doctor took his leave on that New Year's morning,
I went to the window and drew up the blind. It was getting
light. It must be very cold, I thought, as the window was
patterned with frost and I could see the ice glistening on the
road. I felt numb. Poor gentle Bill, why him? If I could have
cried, it might have helped me, but I just stood there and I
knew, as sure as the day was breaking, that Bill would get worse
with the passing of time. No doubt he would manage a light job
for a little while, but after that, well . . . I turned from the
window, determined to see that Bill's life from now on would be
as happy as I could make it.

Dr Thompson was right. It was six months before Bill was
ready for any kind of work. The railway found him a light job
that satisfied the doctor, and when he knew that he was going
to work again, he became more cheerful.

Alastair was ready to leave College, and had accepted the post he wanted near London. We were delighted and knew he would go far, but were worried that he wanted to marry Catherine before starting his new post in August. What could we say, but wish them happiness? Catherine was a nice girl and we both knew she would make him a good wife: certainly she wouldn't hold Alastair back. She was really a lovely girl, but I thought that with his father off work for so long, Alastair could have given a helping hand until we got on our feet and we certainly could have done without a wedding. The twins had to be rigged out, to say nothing of Bill and myself. But young people in love don't think of these things, and who can blame them? I was hurt because I saw that Bill was hurt. He had always spoken so highly of Alastair. 'He will look after you, Mina, if anything happens to me,' he used to say, but I never allowed him to talk of leaving me. I just changed the subject.

'The boys will have to make their own way, Bill, as we did, and you will still be with me when you retire, so neither of us will need help from the boys.'

Andrew started work at Easter with a large toolmaking firm, a few miles outside Glenburn. James would be ready for University soon and we were just waiting for the result of his highers. So Alastair and Catherine were married in August with our blessing and we managed to weather the storm. As Bill always said, 'We've never died a winter yet.'

I knew he worried about his work. Some days, he just couldn't make it, and had to stay at home. My constant companion was Janet who sympathised with me when she thought I needed it, and at the same time, she was very firm when I rebelled against a society whose scientists could invent atom and hydrogen bombs but couldn't give my Bill a pair of new lungs.

'Steady, Mina,' she would say, 'everything is for a purpose.'

What faith she must have, I would think, but I had none, only praying to God when I came to the end of my tether—and what good was that? I would sometimes think of Uncle Dunk and how he had suffered, without complaint. Bill was very like him in many ways. He must have been in pain, because sometimes I would watch him trying to get breath. But when I asked him, he would smile at me. 'No,' he would say. 'No. No pain, and stop being a clucking hen.'

September came round and it was nearly time for James to go to University. 'Isn't it time you made enquiries about your

Student Grant?' I said one morning. He was working during his holidays in a local grocery store and I was preparing breakfast.

'I am not going to University, Mum.'

'Not going?' I said shocked.

'No. I'm joining the Police Cadets. I've filled in an Application Form.'

'But why, James? You have all your highers.'

'I know, Mum, but I wish to join the police and make my career in that field.'

What could I say? I had always promised my sons that whatever careers they followed would be all right with me, so long as they were happy. But as I looked at James his eyes dropped and I knew then why he wished to join the police. If he had gone to University, it would have been a struggle. I would have had to go out to work, and I didn't wish to leave Bill alone in the house all day. So James's decision, taken all on his own, sorted that out.

As time passed, I saw a continuing deterioration in Bill's health. He worked less and less, and was at home all winter, unable to face the weather. Then I knew that it was only a matter of time, a few weeks, perhaps, or if he was lucky a few months.

His breathing became worse. Sometimes, when his whole body was racked with coughing, I thought he was going to choke. All I could do was to keep him as comfortable as possible. Helplessly, I watched my man slowly leaving me. At times I would give way to a fit of weeping, but Bill never saw me like that. I would shut myself in the bathroom rather than let him see. At other times, I prayed that when his time came it would not be like this, struggling for breath, but that he would go gently, without pain.

His mother came down from The Mains with Angus to see Bill. I was glad that Bill had one of his good weekends when she was there, because we never saw her again. She died in her sleep a month later. When the telegram arrived, I left it to Andrew to tell his father, who was very upset, especially when the doctor told him he could not go to the funeral.

'The boys will take my place,' he said sadly.

I tried to keep him as cheerful as possible on the day of the funeral, but my own mind went back over the years when I had first met his mother, and how I had been accepted into the family. Then I thought about the time, after my marriage, when she had stood in my kitchen in Turlum and told me in no uncertain terms to get my marriage sorted out before it was too late. If she had ever known what was wrong, she never said anything, nor did she ever interfere with our lives in any way. On her visits to Glenburn, although she had never approved of my taking Bill and' the children away, she came to like our friends and neighbours. Now she was gone and we would miss her.

Bill was in bed for two or three days after his mother's death, and when he came downstairs the day after the funeral, he looked awfully drawn. A week later, when with Janet, I thought I saw Bill put his hand up and grip his chest. I said nothing at the time, but when I got Janet to myself, I asked her if she had noticed.

'His mother's death has upset him a bit, but he'll be all right in a day or two.' she reassured me, and then changed the subject.

But it was the birth of John, our first grandchild, that gave Bill a new lease of life, and he seemed better. Alastair and Catherine brought John up as often as they could, but the main factor was distance and also, at that time, they were buying their own home.

Bill's slight periods of progress became fewer. On one of Dr Thompson s visits, I asked about Bill's heart. 'Well,' he hesitated, 'as well as can be expected, under the circumstances.' This bucked me up no end. Bill's heart was good. Dr Thompson had said so. At least, that's what I wanted to believe. I refused to face reality and pushed the doctor's actual words to the back of my mind. Bill's heart was good, that was all I wanted to hear.

One evening, when Janet had just left and Andrew was out with his pals, I went to the cellar for coal. The evenings were getting chilly, and our house needed a lot of heating. After bringing the coal up and washing my hands in the kitchen sink, I returned to the sitting room, where I noticed the television was off. I was very surprised at this, as Bill was extremely fond of the TV. There must be a valve or something blown, I thought Bill would never have turned if off. Turned it down, perhaps, if he wasn't interested in what was on, but never off. I hated anything going wrong with the television as it was Bill's only source of entertainment and I was only too pleased to see him coming downstairs again when he was feeling better. 'What's wrong with the television?' I asked.

'Nothing.' Bill was smiling at the surprise on my face. 'I turned it off. It's a long time since we just sat by the fire and had a chat.'

I sat down on the couch beside him, quite delighted. The

monstrosity in the corner of the living room, in my opinion, took up far too much of our attention. I made myself comfortable and looked up at Bill who was looking at a photograph of the boys on top of the television set.

'That's a good photo of our boys,' he said proudly. I nodded, my mind going back to when they were boys at school. 'They were as wild as the heather, Bill. Remember the scrapes and fights they got themselves into,' I said laughing, 'the black eyes, bruises and blood I had to attend to.'

'Yes.' Bill nodded. 'I'm leaving you three fine sons.'

I sat bolt upright. 'Bill, what are you talking about? I won't listen if you talk that way. Leave me three fine sons indeed! We are going to be together for many years yet. You are only fifty, not eighty. Any more of that talk, and I'll turn on the television.'

'Mina, don't bury your head in the sand. You know, and I know, so don't let's pretend with each other any longer.'

'Bill,' I pleaded, 'please don't. You upset me talking like that.'

'All right then, let's change the subject,' he said.

I leaned back on the cushions, feeling more relaxed.

'As married couples go, we have been very happy, don't you think?' Bill said.

I nodded. This was more my line of talk.

'You have been happy, haven't you, Mina?'

'Of course, Bill. What a silly question!'

'I know you've been happy with the boys,' he continued. 'You've given them so much love. But, have you been happy with me?'

'I have just said so, Bill, haven't I?' I didn't know where this line of questioning was leading. It was so unlike Bill to talk like this, and normally, if he wasn't watching television, he was either reading his paper or back-chatting with the boys. I hoped he wasn't going to take one of his bad bouts again. But more was to come.

'I love you, Mina. I think I loved you the moment we met, remember, in the dance hall at Turlum.'

I took his hand and squeezed it gently, too astonished to speak, while he went on. 'Having said that, I want you to know that I know about Craig McKenzie.'

My grip on his fingers loosened and an ice-cold hand seemed to clutch at my stomach and twist it. I couldn't speak, couldn't move. The silence in the room was deafening. A piece of coal slipped down towards the front of the fire and it sounded very loud. The fire sparked and crackled like a whip.

'I have waited a long time for you to tell me all about it,' said Bill, 'and I think it's time you did, don't you?'

What was I to do? Pretend I didn't know what he meant . . . but I knew I couldn't do that. Craig was the only person who had really mattered to me since Uncle Dunk died. My sons had helped to ease the awful longing I had had through all the years I hadn't seen him and the deep respect and admiration I had for Bill helped too. My eyes filled with tears. 'How did you know?' I asked. I couldn't look him straight in the eye and I kept my gaze lowered. My voice hadn't risen above a whisper.

Bill sat looking at me in silence for a few minutes, then continued. 'I had no idea who it was, not at first anyway, but I knew there was someone. I thought to start with that it was my imagination—that was before we were married. But after that, I knew for certain. The way you acted when we first married, told its own story. I gave you every opportunity and waited for you to tell me. I kept asking, if you remember, if there was anyone else, and at no time did you give me a straight answer. It wasn't until we went north to Jean McKenzie's wedding, that I knew who he was. It was sticking out a mile. The moment Craig McKenzie came into the Brae House kitchen he had eyes for no one but you. It was very obvious and when I looked from him to you, it was clear to me and everyone there, that we were looking at two people who only saw each other. Anyone there who never noticed what I saw, must have been blind. But they all knew, didn't they, Mina? They also knew why you two didn't marry. But I don't, and that's what I want you to tell me. I want to know the reason. Curiosity maybe.'

I remained silent. I hadn't raised my eyes from the floor. Bill went on. 'When I first met him, he was married. It's what happened before that that I want to know about. Why, when he loved you, did he marry another girl? What I saw of the man, he wasn't the type to give up something he wanted. Quite the reverse, in fact, So it must have been you who gave him up. Why, Mina?'

I got my voice at last. 'I was never unfaithful to you, Bill, please believe that. I didn't tell you about Craig because I didn't want to hurt you. I tried. Yes, so often I tried, but I couldn't— just couldn't. You knew I didn't love you, Bill. Remember, you said couples got married and love came later.' Bill just sat there staring at me. I wished I could have read his thoughts but his face gave nothing away. 'We have had a good life together, Bill,' I went on. 'You made me a good man and . . .'

He stopped me mid-sentence. 'I know you were never

unfaithful to me, Mina, you don't have to tell me something I already know. But that is not what I am asking you. Tell me about Craig McKenzie.'

I took a deep breath. 'All right Bill, I'll tell you everything.' So, at last, I unburdened myself to this kind, loving man, who had been my husband all these years and knew so very little about me. I told him of my upbringing, of Uncle Dunk, my love for him and my hatred for Aunt Ann because of her cruelty to a defenceless child. I told him of how I had met Craig and of the love that grew between us. About Northfield. Of my love for the Glen and how I had longed with all my heart to return there, but couldn't, as long as Craig and I were not free to be together.

When I had finished, Bill stayed silent for a few minutes while we both sat very still. When he did begin to speak, it was without anger and his face was very calm. 'I'm glad you married me, Mina. You have given me an awful lot of happiness.' Then with a short laugh, 'I was going to say that my gain was his loss, but that wouldn't be right, would it? I have been listening to everything and watching you when you were telling me. You haven't seen him for over twenty years—yet after all that time, when you even mention his name, your voice is gentle and tender. Is he still at this Northfield farm?'

I shook my head. 'No. Remember when Alex, his brother, called to see us at The Mains, well he told me Craig was back at Drumoich. His wife had died some months before Alex's visit.' I was watching Bill and my heart ached for him. Why did he have to ask about Craig, especially just now, when he wasn't at all well. 'Bill, I'm sorry about this. I really care about you an awful lot.' A sob rose to my throat. 'You deserved someone better than me, someone who would have made you really happy.'

'I would never have been happy with anyone else, Mina. You gave me all the love you were capable of giving. This love, as you call it, between you and Craig McKenzie . . . I don't understand and I wouldn't even begin to try.'

Bill was right there, I thought. He would never undertsand such a love. His love was quiet and gentle, not demanding, and for that I was grateful all my married life. With Craig it was different. There was nothing quiet or gentle about him. He was strong, powerful and demanding. At his sister's wedding I knew that neither of us would ever be happy with half measures. That is why, married to Bill, I could never return to the Glen.

I laid my head on Bill's shoulder and he took his hand and

covered mine. In this way we sat, deep in our own thoughts, gazing into the glowing embers of the fire.

We were still in this position when Andrew came in. He looked at us both, then at the television. 'Why isn't the telly on, Mum? I'm starving. Anything to eat?'

I rose reluctantly, switched on the box and went into the kitchen to make supper.

Chapter 48

The days that followed were full of warmth and friendliness. Bill and I were perfectly happy with each other's company, and now that there were no secrets between us I was glad that everything was out in the open. Although he was going to bed earlier, Bill now rose late in the mornings, but I was happier about his health than I had been for some time. When Dr Thompson called on his weekly visit, I said to him, 'If Bill goes on improving like this doctor, you are going to lose a patient.' He smiled and patted me on the shoulder. 'You have been a good nurse.'

Then, one morning, Bill didn't come down at his usual time. To begin with I didn't really notice, being busy in the kitchen baking, but when I went into the sitting room and saw it was half past eleven, I hurried upstairs and into the bedroom. Bill was usually down before eleven.

At a glance, I saw that he was ill, very ill, so I flew to the 'phone. The doctor arrived in record time and examined Bill. 'I think he should go to hospital, Mrs Southall. He will get every attention there. I'll send an ambulance.'

'No,' I said firmly, 'he is staying here. If he is going to die, he will die here, at home.'

'Who said anything about dying?' the doctor asked. He was standing with his back to the sitting room fire.

'Well, isn't he doctor?'

He looked at me for a long time, then ignoring my question said, 'Very well, I'll leave him in the meantime, but when I come back this evening, if he is still having difficulty in breathing you will have no choice but to allow him to go into hospital.'

But he never saw Bill again. That evening was very wet, and Andrew stayed at home watching television while I was upstairs with Bill. At one point I went over to the window and was watching the rain pouring down and the street lights picking out the puddles on the road below when I heard a movement over at the bed and, turning, I saw Bill trying to raise himself up. I was at his side immediately, arranged his pillows and made him as comfortable as possible. His breathing was much quieter.

'That's fine, Mina.' He smiled up at me. 'You have done a bit of running up and down those stairs these last two or three years.'

I put my fingers to his lips. 'All you have to do is to get well and come downstairs again, Bill, that's all I ask. Would you like a drink of water?' I asked, turning to the bedside table and pouring a little water into a tumbler. I turned to give him a drink, raising his head a little, but instead of taking it, he looked up at me, smiled and closed his eyes. He is wanting to sleep, I thought, drawing away my hand from his head. It fell back onto the pillow. I stared hard at Bill's face and if I hadn't known he had passed away, I would have thought he was asleep, so peaceful did he look. That is one prayer I had had answered. Bill's passing had been quiet and without pain.

Chapter 49

The next week was just a blur, a daze. The boys, relations and friends were coming and going. The house was constantly full of people and I never seemed to be alone for one moment. Then everything changed. Just as quickly, the house was empty, except for Andrew and myself. At times, I wanted to run out of the house and away. At other times I didn't want to leave it at all. I encouraged Andrew to go out and find company with his pals. All three boys were shocked because I had kept the truth of the seriousness of their father's illness from them. They had their own lives to live and were young, so why burden them with worry?

Then there were Janet and Charles. Those two wonderful friends have my undying gratitude. What would I have done without them? They didn't crowd me, but when I needed them they were always there. It was Janet I went to when I needed advice about myself or the family.

Chapter 50

James and Marilyn were married two months later, a lovely wedding which I enjoyed very much. James was a fully qualified policeman now, and I had no doubt he would go far. The results of his hard work and his ability to mix theory with practice would bring its own reward. A few weeks after James's wedding, I got my smaller house. The four apartments where I brought up my family was too large for my needs, so I had applied for a smaller one. I thought I would have to wait for ages and it was with some surprise that, after a short time, I received word that there was a smaller house in another part of Glenburn. I was going to begin a new life away from memories of the past. One never forgets, but new environments and new interests help.

I thought the flitting would be a problem, but it was just the same as the day, many years ago when we arrived from Turlum. Friends and neighbours all rallied to the call, helping with the painting and papering of my new home. Then came the furniture, carpets and nicknacks and my old house was scrubbed out awaiting the new tenant.

Before I left it for the last time, I stood looking round the empty house. I had been happy here with Bill's love and my love for the boys. Bill was gone, and the boys had lives of their own. I was going to be alone now with a new life in a new home which had no memories. I was nearly fifty and, at fifty, only sixty sounds old.

'Thanks, Bill, for everything,' I whispered into the silent, empty house. 'But I must look forward now, not back and you would never have wanted me to do anything else.'

I pulled the door firmly behind me.

Chapter 51

When Andrew told me a few weeks later that he had applied for a post in America, I accepted his news as cheerfully as possible and encouraged him in every way. I wasn't going to let him guess that deep down, I feared the final loneliness of his departure.

He was interviewed in a Glasgow hotel and accepted as a

toolmaker, Grade One. Andrew had never been clever in school, but as a toolmaker, few could equal him. His delicate fingers could turn a piece of raw steel into a tool, polished and perfect, right down to a thousandth of an inch. The school teachers' despair had turned into a master craftsman. His medical, passport and visa, were only a matter of form.

The night before he left, a huge party was given for him. What a night it was for him to remember. His friends, their girl friends, and his own old girl friends all came to wish him success. He seldom had had a steady girl friend. On one occasion he had said to me, 'Mum, when the right one comes along, I'll know.'

Somehow I had the feeling that when Andrew did pick his future wife, she would be a good one. But tonight, he was fancy free and happy at the thought of his new adventure. As usual, Charles was in the midst of things, keeping the party going in full swing. He even got Janet to sing—a feat in itself, because although she was a beautiful singer she would never sing in public. All too soon, it came to an end.

Janet and Charles took us to Glasgow Airport where Andrew was to board a plane for London, and then on to the States by jet. I won't break down and embarrass Andrew, I kept saying to myself in the car, I'll just pretend he is going on a wee holiday.

I didn't get the chance to break down. The moment his flight was announced, Andrew picked up his small holdall, the rest of his luggage being on the plane, and without looking at me he just walked straight through the barrier and was gone. I called after him, but he didn't turn.

Charles led the way back to the car, and once inside I gave way to a flood of tears, 'He didn't even look at me Janet,' I sobbed.

'Mina, if Andrew had turned round to say goodbye, he would have cried and you wouldn't have wanted that, would you?'

'Oh Janet, I'm going to miss him so much.'

'After his first letter, you'll be fine. You'll see.' She patted my arm.

It was a week before I received Andrew's first letter and as I read it I felt much easier in my mind. He liked his job and his workmates, and also liked his digs. I wanted to share my joy with Janet, so slipping on my coat, I went down to her house and handed her the letter. 'It's from Andrew,' I said happily.

Janet read the letter and handed it back. 'There you are now what did I tell you?' He is going to do well, and there's the proof.'

I arrived back at the house to see a stranger standing talking to my next-door neighbour and as I approached I heard her say, 'There's Mina now.' The visitor smiled and held out his hand. 'Hallo, Mina.'

I had no idea who he was.

'I'm sorry,' I said, shaking hands, 'but I . . . '

'Mark Dewar,' he cut in.

'Mark, oh I'm sorry, I didn't recognise you.' I put the key in the lock and entered with Mark at my heels and asked him to take a seat. 'After all,' I said, with an embarrassed laugh, 'I only saw you the weekend you were married and a few times in hospital when I visited Mary.' I started to take off my coat while he went on. 'I suppose we've both got a bit older looking, but I recognised you right away.'

'How is Mary, and why isn't she with you?' I asked.

'I lost Mary four years ago.'

'Oh Mark, I'm terribly sorry.' I felt awful. My childhood friend had gone. 'What can I say, except . . .' I didn't know what to say because, it all flooded back to me, the years when I had had my own troubles. 'What happened, Mark?'

'She had tuberculosis. Of course, you knew that, I think.'

'Yes, but I thought that with cure and medical attention, she was going to be all right.' The battle against TB had been fought and won before anybody was really aware of it.

'The cure came too late for her I'm afraid, Mina. The disease was too deep-rooted when the cure was discovered.' Poor Mark. I sat looking at the man who had married Mary thirty years before. How could I have recognised him? His hair was now pure white, his face deeply lined, his cheeks hollow and thin. Too thin, I thought. I could see it hurt him to discuss Mary, so I remained silent, remembering her as she was that morning of her wedding, and how she rode 'Duke' with all the confidence of a good rider. I remembered the jump over the ditch and fence and Mary's triumphant 'Whoopee' as Duke landed after a perfect jump. I remembered how she had looked in all her wedding finery, beautiful, the happiness she felt reflecting in her smile. That was how I wanted to remember Mary.

Mark's voice broke into my thoughts. 'I hear you're a widow.'

'Yes,' I said quietly, 'I lost my husband last year. How did you know?'

'It wasn't until I came into the town and started making enquiries as to your whereabouts that I found out. You see, the last time I was up in the Glen, about six months ago, to see

Peter, my brother-in-law, Craig was there. He gave me your address and asked me to call on my way up, the next time I was down south. I lost the address, but I remembered the town. There was a funny silence. 'Why don't you come up to the Glen with me, Mina, and surprise him?' I shook my head. 'But why not? You have nothing to keep you down here.'

'No thanks, Mark, I'm not ready to go up to the Glen, just yet.'

An hour or so later, Mark took his leave. 'Mary told me all about you and Craig, Mina. You are both free now. You know his wife died?' I nodded.

'When I go north,' he continued, 'and tell Craig that you too are free, he'll be here. So, here's a little advice from someone who has known much happiness. Grasp it this time, with both hands.'

He left, and I can't remember if I said 'Goodbye.'

Chapter 52

Three days later, I was having an early bite when the door-bell rang. I put the lunch under the grill and turned it to low, hoping that whoever it was at the door wouldn't be long. I didn't like cold lunches. It was my hotel training coming back to me. Strange, how the ringing of a bell and the time it takes to open the door can change a whole life. I opened it and faced the tall figure of Craig McKenzie.

Chapter 53

I recognised him instantly. His dark hair was streaked with grey now and I noticed it had thinned slightly at the temples. It suits him, I thought. The strong face underneath, the firm chin and mouth and, as the dark eyes smiled into mine, I noticed the wrinkles at the corners. He had broadened, but very little. I saw his eyes wandering over me, and he must have liked what he saw. We didn't speak. I simply beckoned with my hand for him to enter. He walked past me into the living room and a moment later his arms were outstretched. I threw my arms around his neck and he held me in a vice-like grip. The years rolled back. There was no shyness or embarrassment between us. It was as if we had seen each other only the other day.

When he had loosened his grip and stopped kissing me, he held me away from him, gazing at me, his eyes full of love, and when he spoke, his voice was deep with emotion. 'Mina.' He looked away, and looked back. 'At last.'

I couldn't speak. His arms went round me again pressing me close to his body. I had never been held like that through all these years and had never felt the strength of him since he had last held me in the Brae House, when we said goodbye.

'Craig, oh Craig, is it true?'

He held me away from him again and pushed my hair back from my face. 'Let me look at you.'

'I'm a stone overweight.'

'It suits you,' he said, stroking my face with his hand. 'The only wrinkles I see are laughter lines.'

'Flatterer.'

I wriggled out of his arms, took his hand and drew him over to the settee. 'Sit down, Craig,' I said softly. 'I'll need to switch off the cooker. My lunch will be ruined.'

But instead of sitting where he was, he followed me into the kitchen. 'We will get married as quickly as possible, Mina.'

I switched off the cooker, turned and faced him. 'Must we be married to be together, Craig?'

He shook his head and put his hands on my shoulders. 'No, Mina, we vowed many years ago to love each other until death. Now, over thirty years later, we still feel the same.'

'We don't need a signature on a piece of paper to bind us, Craig,' I said, snuggling up to him.

'Then what are we waiting for? Let's go.'

I looked up at him. 'Go? Go where?'

'To the Glen of course,' he answered simply. 'Naturally.'

The Glen. These words, coming from Craig in his soft Highland lilt, were like music to my ears. Of course—to the glen. Where else? I thought. we met in the glen. Fell in love in the glen. Parted in the glen. And now we were returning to the glen, together.

We moved slowly back to the sitting room, with his arm round me with my head on his shoulder. We sat on the settee.

'Tell me, Craig, has the glen changed?'

'Yes,' he said, 'it has. A lot of it for the best, I think You will see many changes. The glen has become smaller, because travel is faster.'

'But my glen won't have changed, Craig. The mountains will still be there. The Lochs, rivers and deep gorges between the mountains. The moors and the peat bogs. These will never change. The deer will still come down to the foot of the mountains in winter. The eagle will still spread its wings and soar up to the eyrie on the mountain cliff.'

He was watching me with a broad smile on his face. 'How on earth did you manage to stay away so long?'

I rose and went to the window. 'You stopped me. To go up there and not see you would have been impossible.'

'I'm taking you back where you belong.' His voice became firm as I had known it. 'Go and pack some things.' I turned to go upstairs obediently, then stopped.

'But I will have to see my friend Janet to tell her I'm going away. Otherwise she will have the Glenburn police out looking for me.'

He laughed. 'Right, we can tell her as we leave. Do we pass her house?'

I was looking out of the window as Craig was speaking and I could see his car parked outside the gate. 'She is only two streets away,' I answered, and thought I'd better see Janet alone. In my own time I will tell her about Craig, but not yet. Not just yet . . .

'I won't be long, but first I'll make you something to eat,' I said, and turned back to the kitchen.

'No, Mina,' he broke in. 'We will break our journey and have something on the way north, but while you are out, I'll make a cup of coffee and have a snack. Your kitchen isn't very big so I won't be long in finding something for myself.' I went obediently up the stairs.

On the road down to Janet's I wondered if I was dreaming. I could not believe that Craig McKenzie was actually in my house, waiting to take me back to the Glen. I burst in on Janet and, all in one breath said, 'Janet, I'm going away. I don't know when I'll be back. I'll send you a postcard.'

'Wait a minute, wait a minute, what's the rush? Sit down and get your breath.' I threw myself into one of the chairs. 'Now, where are you going? To James's no doubt.'

I looked at Janet. 'I must have forgotten to tell you, Janet.'

'Oh well, have a cup before you go.' She was looking strangely at me.

'I can't Janet, I can't wait.'

'Why not? Who's waiting for you? Where are you going?'

I didn't answer her. I simply held out my hand, took the cup and saucer instead, and gulped some tea to be polite. 'How long are you staying this time?' Janet asked.

'I'm not quite sure,' said I, sipping my tea, not even looking at her. I had never deliberately set out to deceive her, but my whole background was so different from Janet's that she would never have understood. I know she would understand now but it was years too late to explain. The lie about my parentage had been told. I rose. I'll need to go Janet. See you when I come back.'

'Mind that postcard.' I waved. 'Cheerio.'

I was back in record time. Craig was still in the kitchen. 'Have you not eaten yet?' I asked.

'Yes,' he said, 'and thoroughly enjoyed it. I opened a tin of salmon and ate the lot, then cleared away and washed up.'

We both laughed. 'Quite domesticated,' I said lightly.

'Well, on special occasions.'

I ran upstairs and shoved dresses, clothes and footwear into a large case. Thank goodness, I thought, for present-day modern fabrics that don't crush as they did years ago. My personal items were in the bathroom. I wore no make-up, and only used cream and lipstick. I hurriedly drew the comb through my hair. I had lost a lot of my black luxurious hair, but I had a good hairdresser who kept the grey hairs at bay and the confidence of a well-groomed woman who doesn't look her age. And, what's more important, doesn't feel it.

I ran downstairs. Craig was standing at the window. 'If you get my case, Craig, I'll see to everything else.' I wasn't really aware that I was taking over and ordering him about.

I went into the kitchen, collected any food I thought would go stale and threw it into the bin outside the back door, then locked it and made sure the cooker and electricity were switched off at the mains. Craig was waiting for me in the small hall. He opened the door and pushed down the Chubb lock. From the time I had left Janet's until I was sitting beside Craig in the car, had taken a little more than fifteen minutes.

Chapter 54

The big powerful car ate up the miles and in no time we were leaving the towns and villages on the road to Stirling and Perth far behind. Craig was a good driver, steady and sure, his strong hands in full control of the wheel. 'Do you wish to stop here?' he asked, as we approached Perth.

I shook my head. 'No, Craig, let's just go on.'

We left Perth and we started the long haul up to Aviemore. It was then he asked me. 'Tell me, Mina, about your life with Bill and the boys.'

'There is very little to tell, Craig. We were a very ordinary family. Oh, we had our ups and downs, but on the whole, life went smoothly enough.' I went on to tell him about the boys— how they were getting on and that I now had two grandchildren. 'Bill knew all about you, Craig. I never knew that until a month before he died.'

'I could have told you that, Mina.'

'You?' I asked puzzled. 'How?'

'Remember Jean and Peter's reception? Remember you and I went to the Brae House.'?

I nodded. 'Of course I remember, everything.'

'Well, when we returned to the McAndrews,' Bill spoke to me. He didn't say much really, but what was said, made it clear to me that he knew how we felt about each other. "Mina and I leave tomorrow," he said, "don't ever try and see her, for all our sakes. And please don't tell her I said so".'

We remained silent for some time after that and it was Craig who broke the silence. 'It's all behind us now.'

'What about Northfield,' I asked, 'do you ever go?'

When John was old enough, I gave it to him and had no regrets leaving it. It had caused too much unhappiness to too many people.'

'Yet, at one time you loved it.'

'That was before it came between us.'

Dunkeld, Pitlochry and Killiecrankie were soon behind us and we eventually arrived at Aviemore. Craig drew in to a car park beside an hotel. 'Hungry?' he asked.

'Yes, I am. After all, I didn't get my lunch.' I smiled up at him. 'I received a very important visitor instead.'

We got out of the car and, hand in hand, entered the hotel. Craig looked very happy and scarcely took his eyes off me. 'Happy?' he whispered. I nodded. What woman wouldn't be happy, getting her heart's desire after so many years.

We finished our meal and, within an hour, we were on our way again. 'Comfortable?' he wanted to know. 'There is a rug in the back seat if you want it. It gets cold at night.'

I didn't need a rug. The car was lovely and warm. 'We should be in the Glen about nine o'clock,' he said.

I relaxed on the seat beside him and there didn't seem to be any need for talk. By nine o'clock we were crossing the River Ness. It was quite dark, but we had only another twenty odd miles to go. The lights of the car picked out the dark bleak waters of the loch. Craig spoke quietly. 'We are not going to the Brae House, we are going to Drumoich. After all, I met you there and that's where we are going tonight.'

It didn't matter to me. I was in the Glen. I was home. And what's more, Craig was with me. He looked at me and must have seen the look on my face, for in his deep baritone he started to sing in Gaelic. The Hills of Home, the song was called. He remembered that it had been my favourite tune in the old days, and still had beautiful memories for me.

The car eventually swung off the main road and started to climb. A few minutes later, it swung left and stopped. We were at Drumoich. I was surprised to see that the house was all lit up. Craig had said he lived alone. The outside, I noticed, had had a face-lift, but otherwise it looked the same to me—what I could see of it in the dark. Craig took my hand and together we entered the well lighted hall. He took my coat and hung it up. 'You have electricity now,' I said looking up towards the ceiling.

'Yes,' he answered, 'everything is very modern now,' and gave a small laugh. 'I wonder what my mother would have thought of all these modern devices. She would be terrified to switch on the electricity possibly.' I agreed, remembering how set she had been in her ways. 'Would you like something, Mina? Tea or coffee?'

'Just a cup of tea, Craig, please.'

'I asked the cattleman's wife, before I left, if she would see there was a fire on for us and a tray. She acts as my housekeeper. They have no family, so it suits all concerned.' As he was speaking, he opened the door of what I used to know as the parlour, now called the sitting room, and ushered me in. The moment the door opened, I could smell the fragrance of the peat fire. I walked over and held out my hands as if to embrace it. Craig was watching me. 'I'll get the tray.' And in five minutes laid one on the coffee table beside the settee. I was glad of the tea and, sipping it slowly, I looked around the warm cosy room. 'Quite a change from the linoleum,' I said, looking down at the carpet underfoot.

'Yes indeed, Mina. It's the same all through the house, as you will see. I like comfort and I noticed you do too. I rather liked your little home in Glenburn.'

I laid down my empty cup. 'I am so happy to be here, Craig.'

He drew me into his arms. 'Are you really sitting here beside me in Drumoich, Mina? I can hardly take it in. How desperately I wanted you, down through the years. We belong together, you and I. It was here I gave you your first kiss. Remember that morning?'

'I remember everything we ever did together, Craig.' I sat gazing at the peat fire, while my memory slipped back over the years. A small girl between ten and eleven years old had sat at the kitchen table here in Drumoich, opposite a youth of seventeen who gazed at her with admiration in his eyes. Unknown to both of them, the seed of love had been sown, a love that now spanned more than three decades and had survived.

The clock on the mantlepiece chimed the hour of midnight and as the chimes died away, Craig opened the door. I turned. He was standing, his arms outstretched, just inside it. I hurried over and was caught up in his arms, no gentle embrace, but powerful like the man himself, and demanding, and I was the willing partner. This, I thought, is how it will always be between us.

Hand in hand, we ascended the broad staircase. The happiest days of our lives had begun.

Chapter 55

We rose late next morning. After breakfast, which had already been cooked and left in the oven by the cattleman's wife, we got ready to go to the Brae House. Driving up the Glen, Craig asked, 'Well, how do you feel this morning?' It's a beautiful day, isn't it?' 'Wonderful,' I answered. 'But Craig, it's cold and it's raining,' I looked out through the windscreen at the bleak morning, as we laughed happily together.

Dalreich came into view and my school days flooded back to mind. Although I had liked school, as such, I hadn't been very happy there. The glen children had seen to that. I wondered if it was still the same. Ten minutes later, we were in Balgreig. I remembered that someone, somewhere, had said once, 'It's a mistake to return, it's never the same.' And I had a moment of doubt.

The car stopped and Craig jumped out to open the car door

for me. As I got out, Peter and Jean came from the house to meet us. He had changed a great deal and become very stout and, to my way of thinking, had a very unhealthy pallor. Jean, like myself, had worn well, and I would probably have recognised her anywhere. We were asked to stay for dinner. The McAndrew farm steading, like the one at Drumoich, had been rebuilt, but the farmhouse itself was just as I remembered it. The McDonald croft had long been swallowed up by the McAndrews. The McMillan and Fraser crofts at the other end of Balgreig were no longer there.

Another farm stood on the site where Mrs Fraser's croft had been. A very modern bungalow now sat on the boundary between where the Fraser and McMillan crofts were once. Craig had prepared me for some of the changes, and I wasn't as surprised as I might have been, but felt a little nostalgia, perhaps, at the old giving place to the new. But it was to the Brae House that my eyes hastened. From where I stood, I could only see the gable end.

'Give me the key to the cottage, Jean, and I'll take Mina over,' Craig said.

'Aren't you coming in first, Mina? I wanted to have a chat with you,' said Jean.

I shook my head. I resented Jean and Peter having the key of the Brae House. After all, they had once wanted to turn it into a grain store.

As we approached the house, a lump rose to my throat. I could almost see Uncle Dunk sitting at the door in the warm sunshine. The windows and doors were badly in need of a coat of paint, and in place of the corrugated iron roof, there were slates. There was no outhouse or henhouse, just the dwelling-house. Craig put the key in the lock, and the door swung open, while he stood aside for me to enter.

I stood, glued to the doorway. I'm going to make a fool of myself, I thought, and cry, just as I did forty-seven years ago, as a child of three. Swallowing hard, I looked at Craig, who must have sensed my feelings, for he immediately took my hand in his strong grip. Together we entered the lobby that adjoined the kitchen parlour. I had expected to see an empty kitchen and fireplace, had assumed in fact that the whole house would be in a state of decay and dilapidation. So what a pleasant surprise to see the glow of a peat fire! The furniture was exactly as it had been when Craig's mother had stayed there. There was no linoleum on the floor, just the flagstones that I had known so well.

'Thanks Craig,' I whispered, 'for looking after it for me.'

He smiled. 'It's Jean you have to thank, for the fire anyway. I phoned her this morning and said you would be visiting the Brae House. She thought it would be cosier looking.'

'I must thank her when we get back,' I said. 'I admit I resented her having the key of the Brae House, especially after she and Peter had once thought of turning it into a grain store.'

Craig was laughing. 'Alex told me you nearly swallowed him when he mentioned it.' Then he became serious. 'I would never have allowed that, Mina. I knew that some day you would return, and until then, the Brae House was to be left as it was.' He cupped my face in his hand. 'I want you to make up your mind what you want done about it. Has it to be left as it is, or do you want it rebuilt and modernised? No one can make that decision for you, so I'm leaving you for half an hour to wander round the place and see what you think.' He kissed me on the cheek and left.

Alone in the Brae House, I walked over to the window and looked out. There was no garden gate or fence and no garden for that matter. There was just a wilderness where nature had taken over and man had left off and a bramble bush where Mary and I had once played 'houses'. The emblem of Scotland stood tall and straight where Uncle Dunk's roses used to be. I turned from the window and sat on a chair in Uncle Dunk's corner, then looked behind the chair and saw my stool. A burning sensation came into me as I lifted it up. It was my stool all right, there was my name carved out in the left hand corner and Uncle Dunk's on the right.

I remembered that day well. 'Give me your knife, Uncle Dunk,' I had asked.

'What for?' he wanted to know. 'I'm not giving you my knife to cut yourself with.' It was two or three days later that I came home from school and Uncle Dunk was nodding in his chair and there, on the mantlepiece, was his knife, opened, lying beside his tobacco pouch. I grabbed it and taking my stool, went out to the back of the house where I carved our names on the corners.

When I came in, Uncle Dunk was feeling the mantlepiece with his hand. 'See if you can see my knife anywhere, Mina. I thought I left it beside the tobacco.' I handed him his knife and proudly displayed the stool.

He was staring in amazement. 'What in the world made you do that? When Anne sees what you have done . . .' He was at a loss for words, but I wasn't.

'Our names will be on my stool for ever and ever, Uncle Dunk.' I was holding it up for inspection when Aunt Anne passed the window.

'Here she comes, Mina, get that stool behind my chair, quick.' Aunt Anne found out of course, and her wrath knew no bounds. My face was slapped, my hair was pulled and I was thrown to the floor. 'I'll teach you, my girl, to cut up furniture. You are wicked and destructive.'

I picked myself up off the floor and sought refuge behind Uncle Dunk's chair. Once there, I knew I was safe. For all the punishment I had taken, I never one moment regretted what I had done. Several years later, on the underside of the stool, I carved Craig's name. If Aunt Anne ever saw it there, she never mentioned it. My eyes were moist as I replaced the stool gently behind the chair.

I rose and made for the parlour. It was completely empty. I turned and closed the door behind me and went upstairs, up the twelve steps, as I used to call them. Uncle Dunk had taught me to count to twelve with the aid of these steps.

On entering my small attic bedroom, I saw that the paper was peeling off at the side of the skylight window. The rain must be getting in, I thought idly. The home-made dressing table was still there, with the small mirror, the same I had looked into as a teenager, hoping Craig would think me the most beautiful girl in the world the next time we met. I smiled into the mirror at the thought of being beautiful. I was never that. Striking, maybe, but not beautiful.

Leaving my old room, I went to the other attic which had been Aunt Anne's bedroom, which I had seldom entered. I was never encouraged to go there. One incident that I remembered was the day I had been playing with Mary and Mrs Fraser's sons and her two foster girls. I had cut my toe on a piece of glass behind their house. Andrew Fraser examined my toe and jokingly said, 'It's nearly off, Mina.'

I didn't take it as a joke. I took to my heels and ran home, bursting into the kitchen. Nobody was there. Uncle Dunk, at that time, was able to get about with the aid of his crutches and he was in the garden at the back of the house. I was screaming, 'Uncle Dunk, Uncle Dunk, my toe is coming off.' But he can't have heard me.

Instead, a voice from upstairs called, 'What's all the noise about?' It was Aunt Anne. I flew upstairs, still crying, with my toe still bleeding, and burst into her room. She looked at my tear-stained face and then down at my toe. 'Get out of here and

don't stand there blubbing. Look at my floor—blood all over
the place.'

I stared at her and, in my anger, almost forgot my toe.
Standing my ground in defiance, I threw at her, with all the
venom of an eight or nine year old child, 'You are horrible.
I wish you were dead.'

Aunt Anne grabbed me, and hauled me to the top of the
stairs. I was terrified, sure she was going to throw me down.
'Aunt Anne,' I pleaded, 'don't throw me down. I'm sorry, I'll
never say that again. I'm sorry, please don't throw me down.'

It was the deep voice of Uncle Dunk at the bottom of the
stairs that brought Anne to a halt. 'Take your hands off her.
Come down here, Mina.'

I ran downstairs. 'Now, what's the matter?' he asked. I told
him about my toe and what I had said to Aunt Anne. 'That was
very naughty of you, Mina,' he said, once I had finished. 'You
mustn't talk to Aunt Anne like that.' Then he turned to Anne
who had entered the kitchen by this time. 'If you frighten her
like that again, you will have me to deal with.' His voice was
harsh.

In silence, Aunt Anne attended to my toe. 'Hmm, it's only a
scratch,' she said coldly. Never again did I enter that room,
unless I really had to.

I turned away and went downstairs to the kitchen, opened
the door of Uncle Dunk's room and went in. There was the bed,
in exactly the same place. I don't know if it was the same bed or
if Craig's mother had brought one from Drumoich with her
when she came to live at the Brae House. It was one of the few
details I had forgotten. The floor was bare, there was no other
furniture. There really never was much, except for a small chest
of drawers and a chair. There was a mattress on the bed with a
cover over it and I knelt down on the bare floor. It had been a
habit with me as a child when I came into Uncle Dunk's room,
when he wasn't well enough to sit on his chair at the fire. It was
in this position that I used to give him all the news about the
outside world, the outside world being Balgreig and district. It
was the only world I knew then, except for the geography we
got in school, but that was just lessons to me.

I felt the silence in the little room. It was the only part of the
Brae House where I really felt Uncle Dunk's presence after all
these years. I wondered why this tiny room affected me like this.
Perhaps it was the love I knew in it, and Uncle Dunk's faith,
combined with his charity, might have had something to do
with it. Whatever it was, his presence was so strong that I felt

if I put out my hand, I could touch him—he seemed as close as that to me.

I still loved the Brae House, remembering how I longed through the years, to come North to the glen, to walk up Tomnaloich and over to the other side to drink my fill of the vast mountain peaks. I loved them in winter, with their white mantle of pure snow. No man cared to pit his wits against the treachery of the gulleys and gorges in that white wilderness. I loved them in the spring with the melting snow glistening in the sun, the small waterfalls of melted snow pouring down the gulleys to disappear into the deep gorges below. Then the summer warmth, bringing out the purple in the heather, the green bracken, the hazel and rowan and birch trees, nestling in the lower slopes. Above all, I loved the autumn with its browns and golds mingled with the green of the pine trees. No painter could ever capture the true colour of nature, far less perfect it. I had been a lucky girl, brought up among such beauty. All the hostility of Aunt Anne paled into insignificance against the wonder that surrounded me and of course, the love of Uncle Dunk.

I heard a step behind me. Craig had come back. He raised me to my feet. 'I thought I would find you here.' He sat on the bed and drew me down beside him. 'Well, have you made up your mind?'

'I don't want the Brae House rebuilt, nor even modernised, because it would lose its meaning for me. Can you understand that Craig?'

'Yes,' was his answer, 'perfectly. Of course, it's not for me to say, I have given up the Brae House.'

I stared at him. 'You can't mean that, Craig.'

He put his hand into his breast pocket and drew out a piece of paper which he handed to me, saying, 'It's yours, except for one or two signatures.'

I was staring at the paper in his hand. 'Take it,' said Craig, laughing. 'It's the deeds of the Brae House. It's yours.'

I didn't know whether to laugh or cry. I took the deeds, looked at them, then folded them up and handed them back. 'Hold on to them just now, Craig. I want to thank you.'

He put them back into his pocket. A moment later, my arms were round his neck and we both fell onto the mattress. I smothered his face with kisses but it wasn't until his grip tightened and he had started kissing me back that I realised I had thanked him enough. I dislodged myself and rose to my feet. 'Craig, we will need to go to your sister for our dinner. We promised.'

'Damn,' Craig said, rising reluctantly and standing beside me.

We entered the kitchen and as I looked out of the window, I noticed the rain had stopped. Craig was behind me. 'When we have had our dinner,' he said smiling, 'or, after a polite time, we will get back to Drumoich.'

'It's stopped raining now. I would like to go up to Tomnaloich after dinner, before it gets dark.'

'Oh no you don't,' he said sternly. 'You are not going up there in this weather.' He swung round until I was looking straight at him. 'There is plenty of time for that in the summer. Even then, I want you to promise me you will never go alone.' His dark eyes were boring into mine. 'I love you, Mina. If I was to lose you now, it would kill me. There would be nothing left. Promise me.' His voice was almost a whisper.

'Of course,' I said softly. 'I promise. I won't do anything you feel so strongly against.' What I had realized since Craig had brought me back the day before was that Bill and Craig were very much alike in one respect. Up to a point, I would get my own way, but it would only be so far and no further.

Satisfied with my promise, his face relaxed. We looked around the Brae House kitchen where so many events in our lives had taken place. He opened the door, and as we passed through, locked it and handed me the key. The sun had come out.

I turned and looked back at my new home. The rays of the sun struck the two small windows. I thought my heart would burst with happiness and pride. Beside me, his hand in mine, was Craig. He was all I had ever wanted and now, thanks to him, I was to be the proud owner of the Brae House.